Introduction

A: Legal and management

B: Health and welfare

C: General safety

D: High risk activities

E: Environment

Contents

Introduction

Overview

The purpose of this book is to explain the basic health, safety and environmental steps that you, your employer and the site or project that you are working on should be taking.

The content gives easy to understand information and practical guidance. Each chapter starts with a summary of what sites and employers should do for you, as well as what they expect from you.

It has been written to assist operatives and specialists sitting the CITB *Health, safety and environment test*, which is an important requirement when obtaining a construction industry scheme card. The card gives proof that individuals working on construction sites have the required training and qualifications.

GE 707 is also the official supporting document for the CITB Site Safety Plus one-day *Health and safety awareness course*.

Feedback

If you have any comments on the content, suggestions for improvement or extra topics your feedback would be welcome. You can contact us by email or telephone as outlined below.

 publications@citb.co.uk

 0344 994 4122.

Acknowledgements

CITB wishes to acknowledge the assistance offered by the following organisations in the preparation of this edition of GE 707.

- ☑ GoakesSafety Ltd.
- ☑ Montpellier International Consulting Ltd.
- ☑ NPS Property Consultants Ltd.
- ☑ RED Scientific Ltd.
- ☑ Simian Risk Management Ltd.

Work-related injuries and ill health statistics for the construction industry

☑ The construction sector is a major employer accounting for around 6% of the UK workforce.

☑ Construction includes three broad industry groups:
  - civil engineering – covering general construction for civil engineering works, including road and railway construction, and utility projects
  - the construction of buildings – covering general construction of buildings, including new work, repair, additions and alterations
  - specialised construction activities – covering trades that are usually specialised in one aspect common to different structures (for example, demolition, electrical and plumbing installation, joinery installation, plastering, painting and glazing).

☑ The UK construction industry is made up of about 194,000 construction businesses, of which 90% employ fewer than 10 workers.

☑ Approximately 2.65 million people are employed in the UK construction industry. It covers activities including housing, utilities, repair and maintenance, refurbishment, demolition, roofing, shopfitting, mechanical and electrical, plumbing and highways maintenance.

☑ On average 43 construction workers are killed each year due to accidents.

☑ The biggest killer (around half) is falls from height, with an average of seven people dying each year as a result of falling through fragile roofs.

☑ The most common over seven-day injuries are due to manual handling or lifting accidents, followed by slips, trips and falls on the same level, falls from height and being struck by an object.

☑ The construction industry has the largest burden of occupational cancer. Past occupational exposure to known and probable carcinogens is estimated to account for about 5% of cancer deaths and 4% of cancer registrations currently occurring each year in Great Britain.

☑ The most significant carcinogen is past exposure to asbestos, followed by silica, solar radiation, and coal, tars and pitches.

☑ Approximately 5,000 people die each year due to past exposure to asbestos.

☑ Work-related respiratory disease covers a range of illnesses that are caused or made worse by breathing in hazardous substances (such as construction dust) that damage the lungs.

☑ Silica is the biggest risk to construction workers after asbestos. Prolonged exposure to respirable crystalline silica can cause lung cancer and other serious respiratory diseases.

☑ Vibration white finger, carpal tunnel syndrome, noise induced hearing loss and dermatitis are the most common non-lung diseases suffered by those in the construction industry.

☑ In 2014-15 stress accounted for 35% of work-related ill health cases.

 Construction workers (just like you) could die due to work-related ill health, or as a result of an accident, if control measures are not followed.

A message from the Health and Safety Executive

There have been big improvements over recent years in reducing the number and rate of injuries to construction workers. Despite this, construction remains a high-risk industry and accounts for a high percentage of fatal and major injuries.

What is less recognised is that construction is a high-risk industry for health issues too.

Every year more working days are lost due to work-related illness compared to injuries. The statistics reveal that construction workers have a high risk of developing diseases from a number of health issues. Construction has the largest burden of occupational cancer amongst the industrial sectors.

Anyone responsible for putting people to work on a construction site must ensure they have obtained, or are in the process of obtaining, the necessary skills, knowledge, training and experience to carry out the job or task in hand. Being competent is not the same as simply being trained to do a job.

Workers can play a vital role in improving health and safety standards on site. By contributing to the consultation process with both their employer and principal contractor, they can help to prevent dangerous conditions from developing on site. Workers need to develop their skills in identifying risks and be confident in speaking out when they notice that something is wrong.

This *Safe start* publication will help you understand some important points about the risks you face, why the risks are significant and what you and your employers need to do to manage these risks to remain healthy and safe.

Attending a site induction

Setting out

Construction is an exciting industry. It is constantly changing as projects move on and jobs get done. As a result of this, a building site, without the proper management systems and controls, could be a dangerous environment to work in. But accidents and ill health can be avoided if everyone on site works together.

A free online film, *Setting out*, explains what you and everyone on site must do to stay healthy and safe at work.

This film is essential viewing for everyone involved in construction, and should be viewed before you sit the CITB *Health, safety and environment test*. The content of the film is summarised here, and these principles form the basis for the case studies in the test.

Part 1: What you should expect from the construction industry

Your site and your employer should be doing all they can to keep you and your colleagues safe.

Before any work begins the site management team will have been planning and preparing the site for your arrival. It is their job to ensure that you can do your job safely and efficiently.

Five things the site you are working on must do are listed below.

☑ Know when you are on site (signing in and out).

☑ Give you a site induction.

☑ Give you site specific information.

☑ Consult with you on matters which affect your health, safety and welfare.

☑ Keep you up to date and informed.

Part 2: What the industry expects of you

Once the work begins, it is up to everyone to take responsibility for carrying out the plan safely.

This means you should follow the rules and guidelines as well as being alert to all the changes on site.

Five things you must do are listed below.

☑ Respect and follow the site rules.

☑ Safely prepare each task.

☑ Complete each task responsibly.

☑ Know you can and should stop (if you think anything is unsafe).

☑ Keep learning.

Every day the work we do improves the world around us. It is time for us to work together to build an industry that puts its people first. By working together we can build a better industry that respects those who work in it.

Working Well Together in construction

The Working Well Together (WWT) campaign is an industry-led initiative that helps support micro and small businesses improve their health and safety performance. WWT has become the most successful health and safety initiative within the construction industry. The campaign undertakes a variety of work, including health and safety awareness days, designer awareness days, breakfast and evening events, roadshows and regional WWT groups.

Working Well Together campaign posters

The following are aims of the WWT initiative.

☑ Improve health and safety knowledge and good practice and seek to continuously improve health, safety and welfare performance in the construction industry.

☑ Provide practical advice and assistance to the construction industry on the provision and maintenance of healthy and safe working environments.

☑ Encourage co-operation between members in relation to sharing knowledge of health and safety matters.

☑ Promote training and learning in health and safety.

☑ Provide free or low cost information, advice and training to employers and workers in the construction industry.

☑ Stage events where at least half the people who attend will be from small businesses (15 or fewer employees) and 20% from micro businesses (five or fewer employees).

 To find out how the WWT campaign can help you and your company refer to its website: www.uk.com

How to use GE 707

GE 707 follows the standard structure that is used across all core CITB publications.

Section A: Legal and management

Section B: Health and welfare

Section C: General safety

Section D: High risk activities

Section E: Environment

Section F: Specialist activities

Each chapter begins with a summary list of what your site and employer should do, together with a checklist that explains what you should do for your site and employer.

Use of icons

A set of icons stresses important points within the text and also directs you to further information. The icons are explained below.

 Website/further info   Important   Case study

 Example   Good practice   Quote

 Question   Poor practice   Definition

 Ideas   Caution   Checklist

 Notes   Consultation   Video

 Favourite   Guidance

Augmented reality

Augmented reality (AR) technology is used in our publications to provide readers with additional digital content such as videos, images and web-links.

This technology has been used to connect you with extra, complementary content. This can be accessed via your mobile device using the Layar app.

 How to install and use the Layar app

☑ Go to the appropriate app store (Apple or Android) and download the Layar app (free of charge) to your mobile device.

☑ Look out for the AR logo (right), which indicates a Layar-friendly page or image.

☑ Open the Layar app and scan the Layar-friendly page or image (ensure that you have the whole page or the specific image in view whilst scanning).

☑ Wait for the page to activate on your device.

☑ Select one of the buttons that have appeared to access the additional content.

Where can I find augmented reality in this publication?

The table below identifies the pages in this publication that are compatible with augmented reality and the information that can be accessed when an active page is scanned.

Page	Content
Cover	Watch a product demonstration
	Buy related products
5	Watch the *Setting out* film
210	Access the training record

Glossary

Many words and terms that you will hear on a construction site are explained in the main part of this book. The list below includes some more terms that you might come across.

Adhesive. A substance used for sticking things together.

Abrasive wheel machine. A machine, such as a bench-mounted grinder or a disc-cutter, which is used for cutting or grinding materials.

Allergy. A damaging reaction of the body caused by contact with a particular substance.

Asbestos. A naturally occurring, heat-resistant substance that was once used extensively in construction work. Breathing in asbestos particles is harmful to the lungs.

Asthma. An illness that causes difficulty in breathing.

Bacteria. Germs that can cause some illnesses.

Barrier cream. A protective cream applied to your hands before starting work.

Bracing. Scaffold poles that make a scaffold rigid.

Brick-guard. A metal mesh fitted to a scaffold to prevent anything from falling through the gaps between the guard-rails and toe-board.

Cable ramp. A temporary 'hump' laid over a trailing cable to protect it from damage by people or traffic passing over it.

CCTV. Closed circuit television.

CDM. Construction (Design and Management) Regulations.

Cherry picker. A type of mobile elevating work platform (MEWP) on which a passenger-carrying basket is located on the end of an articulating or extending arm.

Consultation. The action or process of formally consulting or discussing (for example, a manager asking you for your input whilst carrying out a risk assessment).

Control measure. Putting measures in place to reduce the risk to an acceptable level (for example, guarding on a machine).

COSHH. Control of Substances Hazardous to Health Regulations.

Crush injuries. Injuries caused by something crushing a part of the body.

Distribution system (electrical). The method that is used to get electrical supplies to where they are needed on site.

Double-handling. Having to move something twice.

Edge protection. A framework of scaffold poles or other suitable barrier erected around an open edge to stop anything from falling over the edge.

Employee. Someone who works for someone else.

Employer. Someone who has people working for him or her.

HAVS. Hand-arm vibration syndrome.

Hazard. Anything that has the potential to cause harm (ill health, injury or damage).

Health and Safety at Work Act 1974. The main piece of health and safety law.

HFL. Highly flammable liquids.

HSE. Health and Safety Executive.

HSE inspector. An official who can inspect the site and take action if work is not being carried out safely.

Lanyard. A length of fabric that connects a safety harness with a fixed strong-point.

Ligament. A band of tough body tissue that connects bones or cartilage.

LPG. Liquefied petroleum gas.

Method statement. A step by step description of how to carry out a job safely.

MEWP. Mobile elevating work platform.

PAT. Portable appliance testing.

PPE. Personal protective equipment.

RCD. Residual current device.

Risk. The likelihood of an event occurring from a hazard.

Risk assessment. A document identifying the hazards, risks and control measures for a particular activity.

RPE. Respiratory protective equipment.

Scissor lift. A type of MEWP with a platform that rises vertically.

Slewing. Part of an item of plant (such as the jib and counter-weight of a crane), rotating about a vertical axis.

Solvent. Chemical used to dissolve or dilute other substances.

Tripping hazard. Items lying around that you might trip over.

Ventilated. Supplied with fresh air.

01
General responsibilities

A
01

What your site and employer should do for you

1. Provide a safe place to work.

2. Provide safe plant and equipment, safe substances and materials, safe methods and systems of work, and safe and competent persons to work with.

3. Eliminate or avoid risks where possible.

4. Tell you about the hazards and the risks and how they will be eliminated or controlled.

5. Provide information, instruction and training so you can do your job safely and in safety.

6. Communicate with you and allow you to have your say.

What you should do for your site and employer

1. Follow the site rules and your safe system of work.

2. Avoid taking short cuts or risks.

3. Go to and take part in safety inductions and briefings.

4. Co-operate and get involved.

5. Follow all method statements and precautions.

6. Report anything you think is unsafe.

7. Ensure protective clothing and equipment is used correctly.

8. Report any damage or faults with protective clothing and equipment.

Introduction

Everyone on a construction site is legally and morally responsible for health and safety.

By knowing what is needed, you will be able to understand what you and your employer's legal duties are in respect of protecting yours and other people's health and safety while at work.

A 01

This chapter will help you understand the following.

☑ What the law requires from everyone.

☑ Employers must provide a safe place of work.

☑ Safe systems of work must be planned for, put in place and followed.

☑ People at work must be trained, competent and involved in protecting their own and other people's health and safety.

☑ Communication has to be open, effective and honest so everyone knows what is expected of them.

☑ The Health and Safety Executive (HSE) can and will enforce the law in respect of health and safety.

 Competence

A combination of a person's training, knowledge, experience and skills and their ability to apply these to carry out a task safely. Other factors (such as attitude and physical ability) can also affect competence.

What the law requires

The Health and Safety at Work Act 1974 was introduced to protect the health and safety of everyone at work.

Your employer is responsible for the following.

☑ Protecting all their employees' health, safety and welfare at work.

☑ Providing and maintaining plant and systems of work that are safe.

☑ Ensuring the safe use, handling, storage and transport of articles and substances.

☑ Providing information, instruction, training and supervision, and communicating these effectively.

☑ Maintaining any place of work under their control in a condition that is safe and without risk to health.

The Health and Safety at Work Act imposes a legal duty on you as an employee. This means **you** have a **legal duty** to work safely, protect your own health and safety and that of other people who may be endangered by your acts or omissions. You also have a legal duty to cooperate with your employer in respect of ensuring health and safety.

A
01

> The Health and Safety at Work Act states that the employer must give every worker certain health and safety information. Employers can either display a health and safety law poster or give every employee a card or leaflet with the information on it.

Providing safe ways of working

The law requires employers to develop safe systems of work (a defined method of carrying out each job in a safe way).

The following documents can form part of the safe system of work.

Safe working methods prevent accidents

- ☑ Health and safety policy.
- ☑ Risk assessments.
- ☑ Method statements.
- ☑ Construction phase plan.
- ☑ Results of surveys (for asbestos, noise, and so on).
- ☑ Health surveillance.
- ☑ Permit to work.
- ☑ Minutes of health and safety meetings.

Health and safety policy

Your employer's policy will give you the following information.

- ☑ Explain how health and safety is managed in your company.
- ☑ Identify what the arrangements are (how and what should be done).
- ☑ Show who is responsible for doing what (including what you and your fellow workers must do).

Risk assessments explain the following.

- ☑ The hazards of the work site or task (for example an open excavation).
- ☑ The significant risks (for example people falling in).
- ☑ The controls needed to minimise the risk to an acceptable level (for example erect a double handrail around all sides of an excavation and make sure excavations are adequately lit at night).

Your employer should assess the risks to both you **and** others arising from the work being done.

Method statements explain how the job is to be done safely and in safety. They will also identify the following.

- ☑ The sequence, method and controls to be followed.
- ☑ The materials and equipment to be used.
- ☑ The number of people and skills needed.

☑ A *hazard* is anything that could cause harm to you or another person, (such as chemicals, working from a ladder, or electricity).

☑ The *risk* is the chance (likelihood) that you, or someone else, could be harmed by the hazard and how serious any harm could be.

A
01

Permit to work

☑ A permit to work system is used for controlling high risk activities (such as working on live electrical cables) or where there are activities that need extra controls (such as hot works, confined space entry and breaking the ground (permits to dig)).

☑ A permit to work has strict controls and limitations which must be followed.

☑ You must never start any job for which a permit is needed before the permit's start time and before the controls are in place.

A **construction phase plan** is required for every construction project, it must be regularly reviewed and may be added to or changed as the project goes ahead. It will give you the following information.

☑ The identity and location of the main dangers on site and how they will be controlled.

☑ Describe how the work has been planned with safety in mind.

☑ Explain how the site will be organised.

☑ Explain how people will work safely together.

Survey results

There are a number of surveys (for example, an asbestos, noise or underground services survey) that may be required. The results of these surveys will form part of the safe system of work, as they will show where certain hazards may be.

Health surveillance allows for the signs of ill health to be identified early. It may be needed if you are exposed to a hazardous agent or if your work may have an adverse effect on your body (for example, hearing damage if you are working in a noisy area). It lets your employer check that their control measures are working and that you are not exposed to any ill health that could be prevented.

 Do you follow a safe system of work?

Are you familiar with your safe system of work? Do you know what the sequence of work is? Are you aware of the hazards? Do you have the right equipment and training?

Do you fully understand the identified control measures? Or are you doing it the way you have always done the job, the way you think it should be done or just having to make do with what you have got?

If you are working differently from the written and approved safe system of work then speak to your supervisor or employer. Your way may be better, quicker or more efficient but it may have other risks that you don't know or haven't thought about. The system of work will need to be assessed and if necessary extra controls put in place.

People need to be trained

The law needs you to have the neccessary **training**, **knowledge**, **experience** and **skills** so you can carry out the tasks given to you safely. You should never be put in a position where you have to carry out a job for which you do not have the necessary competence or equipment.

If you think you are, then you may be putting yourself or others at risk – you need to speak to your supervisor or the site manager.

Sharing information and knowledge

Good communication of health and safety information is essential for everyone.

Employers have a legal duty to consult with their workforce. To be effective it needs to be two way (both sides listening, as well as talking).

This can be done in a variety of ways.

- ☑ Site inductions.
- ☑ Posters.
- ☑ Safety briefings.
- ☑ Toolbox talks.

- ☑ Informal chats/open door policies.
- ☑ Worker involvement schemes.
- ☑ Suggestion boxes.

Site induction

You must attend a site induction for each new site that you visit. As a minimum you should be told about the following.

Site inductions are critical for good health and safety communication

- ☑ The site rules.
- ☑ The site hazards (for example, overhead power lines).
- ☑ Traffic management systems.
- ☑ Areas of the site where you can and cannot go.
- ☑ Welfare facilities.
- ☑ Emergency and first-aid arrangements.
- ☑ Personal protective equipment (PPE)

- ☑ Permits to work.
- ☑ Environmental considerations and requirements.
- ☑ How you will be consulted regarding health and safety matters.

Toolbox talks

These are short health and safety briefing sessions on a particular subject connected to the work being carried out.

The person delivoring the toolbox talk should give you the opportunity to ask questions or raise concerns.

 The aim of a toolbox talk is to give and share information to keep you safe and protect your health.

Worker involvement

Workers are often the best people to understand the risks in their workplace. Talking to, listening and co-operating with each other can help in the following ways.

 Identify joint solutions to problems.

☑ Raise standards.

☑ Reduce accidents and ill health.

☑ Help people to work safely and in safety.

You may be asked to take part in site inspections or audits and discuss your usual work methods. This will help your employer understand any problems you are experiencing and propose solutions.

👍 **Have your say**

Many sites run suggestion schemes, regular safety forum/meetings and open door policies.

Please get involved – your views are important and can make a difference.

How the Health and Safety Executive enforces the law

The Health and Safety Executive (HSE) is a Government body responsible for overseeing most aspects of workplace health and safety in the UK. The HSE's main roles are listed below.

☑ Offer advice on workplace health and safety.

☑ Carry out workplace inspections.

☑ Conduct serious accident investigations.

☑ Carry out enforcement action for health and safety breaches.

The HSE has the following powers.

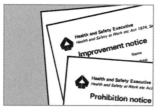

HSE inspectors can issue notices if they think it necessary

☑ The legal power to demand entry to the workplace without notice.

☑ Can interview you or anyone else, with or without caution.

☑ Can prosecute a company, an employer or an **individual employee**.

☑ Can raise and issue improvement or prohibition notices, on an employer or an individual worker. Such notices must be complied with.

☑ Can charge the employer a fee for intervention.

☑ Can measure, take photographs, samples or possession of anything, if required for evidence.

☑ Can inspect record books and any other documents.

☑ Can demand that the scene of an accident remains undisturbed.

Improvement notices

These are issued if something is unsafe, not up to standard or not being adequately controlled. They will say how, in the HSE inspector's opinion, the law was being broken and give a date by which things must be put right or improved.

Prohibition notices

These are issued when, in the inspector's opinion, something is so unsafe that all work connected to it must **stop** immediately, and must **not** start again until the matter has been put right.

Fee for intervention

The HSE can charge an hourly rate for the time the HSE inspector spends investigating a material breach of health and safety law, including visits, letter writing and ensuring that the matter has been put right.

02
Accident reporting and recording

Accident reporting and recording

What your site and employer should do for you

1. Put measures in place that allow different trades to work safely together.

2. Provide an accident book and make sure records are kept.

3. Make sure that accidents, incidents and occurrences of work-related ill health are reported.

4. Listen, and make sure any concerns you have are acted on.

5. Make sure accident and incident investigations are carried out, to find the cause and understand what went wrong so it can be prevented from happening again (to find the cause, not to find someone to blame).

What you should do for your site and employer

1. Understand and follow your safe system of work.

2. Stop and take advice if you cannot follow your safe system of work.

3. Report any accident you have and enter it into the accident book.

4. Report any near misses or anything you think could be unsafe.

5. Co-operate with any investigation.

Introduction

 On average 43 construction workers are killed each year due to accidents.

Over half of the fatal injuries to workers are from three types of incident:

- ☑ falls from height
- ☑ being struck by a vehicle
- ☑ being struck by a moving or falling object.

Year after year the same types of accidents and incidents are repeated.

Common types of accident and incident

- ☑ Falling from height.
- ☑ Slips, trips and falls on the same level.
- ☑ Manual handling.
- ☑ Being struck by mobile plant.
- ☑ Contact with electricity.
- ☑ Contact with moving machinery.
- ☑ Being trapped by something collapsing.
- ☑ Being injured in overturning vehicles and plant.

In many cases these accidents could have been avoided by taking simple precautionary measures (for example, clearing up the work area regularly to reduce the likelihood of slips, trips and falls).

Prevention – what you can do

- ☑ Make sure you fully understand the safe system of work.
- ☑ Work to the instructions you are given.
- ☑ Follow the site rules.
- ☑ Do not be tempted to take short cuts.
- ☑ Keep your work and storage areas tidy (good housekeeping).
- ☑ Keep access routes and walkways clear of materials and equipment.
- ☑ Report anything you think may be unsafe to your supervisor.

All accidents and incidents should be reported. Your employer can then determine the cause and prevent them from happening again.

 Everyone on site has a responsibility to report unsafe conditions.

Accidents

You must make sure that any accident or injury you have is reported and recorded in the accident book. Unsafe conditions and near misses should also be reported, so action can be taken to prevent them from becoming an accident. More serious accidents and those that result in more than seven days off work have to be reported by your employer to the HSE.

Unsafe conditions

Something with the potential to cause harm

Near misses

An incident that nearly resulted in an injury or damage

Accidents

An incident that causes physical injury

The following details **must** be recorded in the accident book.

- ☑ The injured person's name and address.
- ☑ The injured person's occupation.
- ☑ Date and time of the accident.
- ☑ Where the accident happened.
- ☑ How the accident happened.
- ☑ The injury that was sustained.
- ☑ Details of the person filling in the book (if different from the injured person).

Your employer must keep accident book information secure, as it is confidential.

If you see something which is unsafe or witness a near miss it is important you tell your supervisor or employer.

If more unsafe conditions and near misses were reported, it is likely there would be fewer accidents.

You may think reporting them will get you into trouble – but the opposite is true.

Occupational diseases

You must tell your employer if you develop signs or symptoms of the following conditions, or if a medical professional tells you that you are suffering from a condition or disease that they think may be related to your work.

- ☑ Hand-arm vibration syndrome (for example from using hand-held vibrating tools).

- ☑ Cramp in the hand or forearm.

- ☑ Carpal tunnel syndrome from vibrating or percussive tools.

- ☑ Tendonitis or tenosynvitis in the hand or forearm (for example from repetitive or frequent movement).

- ☑ Occupational dermatitis (which, for example, you can get from working with cement).

- ☑ Occupational asthma from breathing in construction dust.

- ☑ Occupational cancer (for example from exposure to asbestos or silica dust).

- ☑ Disease caused by exposure to a biological agent (for example leptospirosis (Weil's disease)).

A
02

03
Health and welfare

What your site and employer should do for you

1. Identify work activities that could damage your health.

2. Tell you about the hazards and risks and how they will be controlled.

3. Provide equipment and safe methods of working to minimise any exposure.

4. Provide you with personal protective equipment (PPE), free of charge, where required.

5. Provide good, clean welfare facilities.

B
03

What you should do for your site and employer

1. Understand how the hazards can damage your health.

2. Use the equipment provided properly and follow the safe system of work.

3. Wear your personal protective equipment (PPE) properly.

4. Do not misuse the welfare facilities and help to keep them clean and tidy.

5. Report any changes in your health.

6. If you have any concerns or any doubts about anything related to your work, raise the matter with your supervisor or manager.

Introduction

Work-related ill health has devastating consequences for individuals and their families, this is often misunderstood and underestimated.

This may be because the effects of exposure to most work-related ill health hazards are not always immediate (unlike an accident which causes an immediate injury). You may go home from work feeling more or less the same each day and are unaware of the effects.

If you are repeatedly exposed to small doses of dust, fumes or certain substances, exposed to loud noises or use vibrating tools, they may cause damage to your body. It can take many weeks, months or even years before symptoms of exposure and damage become a problem to you and by then irreversible damage may well have occurred.

B
03

Common causes of work-related ill health

Respiratory (breathing) diseases

 Refer to Chapter B07 for information on respiratory diseases.

Noise and vibration

 Refer to Chapter B08 for information on noise and vibration.

Skin conditions

Dermatitis

This is a skin condition that is generally caused by exposure to chemicals and other harmful substances. Hands and forearms are most often affected. It can be painful and will affect your personal life as well as your work life.

Dermatitis showing crusting and thickening of skin

Some of the symptoms are shown below.

☑ Redness.

☑ Itching.

☑ Dryness.

☑ Cracking or blistering.

The most common cause of dermatitis in the construction industry is working with cement. Wet cement can also cause burns.

 Allergic dermatitis can make your skin so sensitive you will not be able to use some substances again, which could end your career.

Skin cancer

The number of skin cancer cases continues to increase every year. Those who work outdoors are at a greater risk.

The following actions will help to prevent overexposure and reduce the likelihood of occurrence.

☑ Covering up exposed skin by wearing suitable loose, long sleeved and long legged clothing and a hat.

☑ Using sun block on exposed arms, face and neck.

You should drink plenty of water to prevent dehydration.

 If you notice new warts or moles, or changes to existing moles or they begin to itch, seek medical advice as soon as possible. Don't ignore it – early treatment is vital.

Although less common, skin cancer can be caused by contact with mineral oils. Daily contact with items (such as oily clothing or gloves) can lead to a form of skin cancer. Mineral oils are common on mechanical plant and pipe threading machines.

Diseases carried in the blood

Leptospirosis (Weil's disease)

☑ This disease is carried by **rats** or **dairy cattle**. It enters the bloodstream through cuts and grazes.

☑ It is a particular problem when working on or near water, sewage, waterlogged sites or rat infested areas.

You can minimise the risks by taking the following precautions.

☑ Wear suitable gloves.

☑ Keep all cuts and grazes covered with a waterproof plaster.

☑ Wash your hands before eating or smoking.

Wherever possible discourage rats from coming onto site by using the welfare/canteen facilities provided and putting all food waste in covered bins.

 The early symptoms of Leptospirosis (Weil's disease) are like influenza (flu). If left untreated the disease may lead to kidney problems and can be fatal.

Tetanus (lockjaw)

☑ This is a disease of the nervous system.

☑ It enters the body through cuts, grazes or puncture wounds.

☑ Germs are found in contaminated soils or manure.

☑ An early symptom is an increasing difficulty in opening the mouth or jaw.

B
03

Hepatitis

☑ Hepatitis is usually caught from contact with infected needles and syringes.

– If you find any suspected drug taking equipment leave it alone and contact your supervisor or employer.

Legionella

This is a form of pneumonia, which can be caught by breathing in contaminated water vapour/mist (for example, from air conditioning and cooling towers or hot and cold water systems).

A safe system of work is needed if a water system is suspected of being contaminated by the legionella bacteria.

If you think you may be suffering from hepatitis, tetanus or legionella, get medical advice and tell your supervisor.

Stress and mental health at work

Stress is the adverse reaction people have to too much pressure or other demands placed upon them. It is not an illness in itself, but can lead to you not being able to perform at work and have an impact on your health and wellbeing. Stress can lead to anxiety and depression as well as chronic health conditions such as strokes, back pain, headaches or migraine, stomach problems and drug and alcohol dependency.

Work-related stress and mental health conditions are closely linked with similar signs and symptoms. Work-related stress can trigger or worsen an existing mental health condition. Your employer should identify any signs of mental health problems quickly and efficiently so they can help you access the support or treatment needed.

Stress can affect you physically and mentally

The following may help to improve your mental health.

☑ Talk to a family member, a trusted friend or colleague or someone independent. Talking about how you feel is not a sign of weakness and having someone listen to you can often make you feel better.

☑ Look after your physical health. Good mental health is directly linked to good physical health. Physical activity, sleep and diet can all impact on your mental health.

☑ Do things that you enjoy (for example, a hobby, reading or sport) and try to avoid things that you don't.

☑ Recognise your limits, as this will help you recognise the things that are likely to have a negative impact on your mental health.

Other sources of help are available. For further information refer to organisations such as Mind (www.mind.org.uk), Time to change (www.time-to-change.org.uk) and Bipolar UK (www.bipolaruk.org).

Drugs and alcohol

B
03

Some over-the-counter medicines (such as hay fever medicines or cold remedies) can make you drowsy or have other side effects. This could mean you are not safe to be on a construction site or not fit to drive or operate machinery. You should read the label or speak to the pharmacist if in doubt.

Many employers and clients have policies to carry out random testing for drugs and alcohol.

Anyone caught working under the influence of illegal drugs, psychoactive substances (known as 'legal highs') or alcohol may have to leave site immediately and could lose their job.

Illegal drugs

People under the influence of illegal drugs are a danger to themselves and everyone else on site. They are likely to suffer from the following.

- ☑ Poor or irrational decision making.
- ☑ Slow reaction times.
- ☑ Clumsiness.
- ☑ Distorted vision.
- ☑ Mental confusion.

The effects and traces of some drugs can stay in the body for long periods, even after users think the effects have worn off (for example cannabis can be detected during testing several weeks or even months after it has been taken). Unlike alcohol, there are no permitted safe levels for illegal drugs so a trace could mean failing a drugs test. This includes drugs referred to as 'legal highs' (psychoactive substances).

Legal highs (psychoactive substances)

Legal highs (psychoactive substances) are designed to produce similar effects to drugs (such as cannabis, cocaine and ecstasy), whilst remaining chemically different enough not to be subject to control under the Misuse of Drugs Act. These (psychoactive) substances are illegal under the Psychoactive Substances Act, and may contain one or more substances that are illegal to possess.

It is an offence to possess with intent to consume, produce, offer to supply, possess with intent to supply, import or export any substance for human consumption which is capable of producing a psychoactive effect.

Alcohol

Depending upon your employer or site policy the blood alcohol level needed to pass a test can be less than the legal driving limit.

Besides being a danger to themselves and others, anyone under the influence of alcohol at work risks losing their job and livelihood. Many of the people convicted of drink driving were driving the morning after drinking the night before. Most people seriously underestimate the length of time it takes to sober up.

 The effects of alcohol can last for hours

On average it takes one hour for your body to get rid of one unit of alcohol.

A unit is the volume (litres) x ABV (% alcoholic strength of the drink).

☑ One pint of beer at 5% strength is 2.8 units.

☑ Five pints of beer at 5% strength is 14 units.

☑ One 175 ml glass of wine at 12% strength is 2.1 units.

☑ One 25 ml shot of a spirit at 40% strength is 1 unit.

☑ One 275 ml bottle of alcopop at 5% strength is 1.4 units.

If someone started drinking at 7 pm and drank five pints of beer with a strength of 5% it could be up to 10 am the next morning before all the alcohol is out of their system. However, this time can change depending on things like your size, weight, age and when you last ate.

B
03

 There is no safe limit of alcohol that you can consume and then drive or operate machinery safely.

Welfare facilities

Your employer has a legal duty to provide adequate welfare facilities.

☑ An adequate number of separate toilets for men and women (where this isn't possible, toilet doors should be lockable and separate from urinals).

☑ Toilet paper.

☑ Sanitary disposal facilities for women.

☑ Adequate and suitable hand-washing facilities (not the canteen or kitchen sink), to include running hot (or warm) and cold water, soap or hand cleaner, and a way of hygienically drying the hands.

☑ Showers, if necessary. (Where showers are necessary there should be separate showers for men and women, unless it is a single shower with a lockable door.)

☑ Changing and drying rooms, with separate facilities for men and women, where necessary.

☑ Somewhere to take breaks from work, with a supply of clean drinking water and cups, or a drinking water fountain.

☑ A means of boiling water for drinks.

☑ Chairs with back support (not canteen benches).

Health and welfare

☑ A facility to warm up food (for example a microwave).

☑ A means to secure valuables and change of clothes (for example lockers).

Welfare facilities must be kept clean and in good order. If they are not, then speak to your supervisor or the person responsible.

 The same level of welfare facilities must be made available for transient (mobile) workers.

B
03

Site canteen area for taking breaks

 Welfare facilities are provided for your benefit – please look after them.

04

First aid and emergency procedures

What your site and employer should do for you

1. Tell you the first aid and emergency procedures during the site induction.

2. Maintain emergency escape routes and equipment.

3. Provide first aiders and develop first-aid procedures.

4. Display emergency information, contacts and telephone numbers.

5. Provide emergency and rescue equipment.

B
04

What you should do for your site and employer

1. Be aware of the emergency procedures relating to your own work place and safe system of work.

2. Know how to raise the alarm.

3. Know where and how to get first aid.

4. Know what to do in an emergency or site evacuation.

5. Know where to gather if there is an emergency.

Introduction

Every site should have procedures in place in case of an emergency, such as fire, serious injury, collapse, people trapped or needing rescue or chemical spill.

You must know the following information.

☑ How to raise the alarm.

☑ Where to go and what to do.

☑ What the alarm sounds or looks like.

☑ The escape or evacuation route.

Information should be given during site induction and displayed on noticeboards or signs.

Remember – sites are constantly changing and so can emergency escape routes.

 Make sure you always know your escape route and where any equipment you may need is kept.

You should also be familiar with any emergency procedures that form part of your safe system of work (such as confined space entry and rescue from height).

First aid

During your site induction the following information should be explained.

☑ Where to find the first-aid kit.

☑ Who the first aider and/or appointed first aid person is.

☑ How to contact or recognise the first aider and/or appointed person (for example green hat or sticker on hard hat).

☑ Where to get first-aid treatment.

First-aid post

The primary aims of first aid are to save life, prevent an injury from worsening, and promote recovery, whether or not the injury was caused by the work.

Discovering a casualty

What you can do

If you are first on the scene of an accident your actions could be crucial.

You should do the following.

☑ Assess the situation.

☑ **Make sure you do not put yourself in danger.**

☑ If it is safe to do so remove or isolate the hazard.

☑ Go to the casualty and find out what's wrong.

☑ **Call for help** – if no-one comes explain to the casualty that you are going to go and find help and call the emergency services.

☑ Return and stay with the casualty until help arrives.

It is crucial that time is not wasted. The priority is getting help (first aid) and the emergency services to the injured person as soon as possible.

What employers must provide

B
04

Accidents and injuries do happen on site and employers must provide the following.

☑ Adequate first aid cover at all times when the site is in operation, including shift work, which may mean appointing trained and competent people to act as first aiders or emergency first aiders, and making sure they are available at all times the site is occupied.

☑ Sufficient and suitable first-aid equipment for the hazards and the risks identified (for example, eyewash and burns kits).

☑ Arrangements for lone workers or when the first aider is not there a means to summon an ambulance or other professional help.

They should also take into account how far the site is from a hospital or the emergency services.

First aid roles

Based on the findings of their assessment of first aid needs, an employer could choose to provide first aid cover by appointing one or more of the following roles.

☑ **Appointed person first aid** – is appointed when a first aider is not needed in the workplace. They do not have to have first-aid training as their job is to look after the first-aid equipment and facilities and call the emergency services if needed.

☑ **Emergency first aider** – trained to give emergency first aid at work (EFAW) to someone who is injured or becomes ill.

☑ **First aider** – trained in first aid at work (FAW) and able to provide first aid for a greater range of injuries and illnesses to someone who is injured or becomes unwell at work. Sometimes there may be other hazards on site, for example working in confined spaces; therefore extra training may be needed.

If you use any first-aid equipment you must inform the person responsible for managing it; the first aider, the appointed person or your supervisor.

05

Personal protective equipment

Personal protective equipment

What your site and employer should do for you

1.	Identify risks and eliminate them where possible.
2.	Where there is still a risk, personal protective equipment (PPE) which protects you from those risks must be provided.
3.	Show you how to correctly wear and care for your PPE, and where it should be worn.
4.	Supply PPE free of charge.
5.	Provide facilities to clean, store and maintain PPE.

B
05

What you should do for your site and employer

1.	Wear your PPE at all times when needed.
2.	Wear the right PPE for the task, wear it properly and make sure it is properly adjusted.
3.	Look after your PPE as instructed. (Care for it and it will care for you.)
4.	Report any PPE defects. Damaged, worn out or ill-fitting PPE will not protect you.

Introduction

Personal protective equipment (PPE) consists of items of equipment and clothing designed to protect you from a variety of hazards. The type of PPE that is designed to protect you from respiratory (breathing) hazards, such as the inhalation of dust and fumes, is called respiratory protective equipment (RPE).

Your employer must ensure the following.

☑ A risk assessment is carried out to identify any hazards and risks, and what can be done to eliminate or control them without using PPE.

☑ You are supplied with PPE free of charge, told why it is needed, (whenever there is a hazard that cannot be eliminated or minimised to a safe level by other methods), how to adjust, fit and wear it, and what to do if it is damaged or lost.

☑ You use the PPE supplied as and when necessary and in line with the information and instruction given.

B
05

  PPE should only be used as a last resort.

Policies and site rules

Some sites have mandatory PPE policies or rules, which require the use and wearing of head, eye and hand protection. This is because site workers and visitors can be exposed to a variety of hazards and risks, which can change daily and can be outside the control of the employer or site management.

On most sites you can only take off PPE when you are in a safe area (such as the site office or welfare compound).

Wearing a combination of PPE

Some common examples of PPE are listed below.

☑ Safety helmets (hard hats).

☑ Safety footwear/boots.

☑ High-visibility clothing.

☑ Safety glasses (low-impact eye protection).

☑ Gloves.

There are times when you will need to wear other extra PPE, as identified in the following circumstances.

☑ From site rules/site induction.

☑ Instructions from your supervisor or employer.

☑ As a result of a risk assessment or a direction in a method statement.

☑ As directed by signs and notices.

Other task-specific PPE is listed below.

- [✓] High-impact eye protection (for example, when using a disc cutter).
- [✓] Ear defenders (muffs) or earplugs.
- [✓] Safety harnesses and lanyards.
- [✓] Knee pads and overalls.
- [✓] Wet weather clothing.
- [✓] Lifejackets or buoyancy aids.

Task-specific RPE includes half or full face respirators.

B 05

Your employer must provide the PPE, but you must be responsible for it and for wearing it properly.

- [✓] Take care of your PPE (keep it clean and inspect it regularly).
- [✓] Use your PPE as instructed.
- [✓] Stop work and report any lost or damaged PPE to your supervisor.
- [✗] **Do not** work without it where it is needed.

Types of personal protective equipment

Head protection

Safety helmets must be worn at all times, except when you are in an area declared as a safe area by site management.

A safety helmet is worn to protect you from falling objects or bumping your head. Your safety helmet will be most effective when you follow the guidelines below.

Safety helmet to help protect against head injury

- [✓] Wear it the right way round (peak at the front).
- [✓] Adjust it so it fits snug and square on your head.
- [✓] Make sure it is fitted and worn with a chin strap if there is a risk of it falling off while working.
- [✓] Make sure it is fitted with a proprietary liner for cold weather (do not wear it over your woolly hat).

Do not cut, drill holes, paint or apply unauthorised stickers to your safety helmet, as this can severely reduce its capacity to protect you in an incident.

Do not wear hoodies or beanies under your hard hat. If extra comfort is needed to keep you warm an approved manufacturer's lining should be used.

Dropping your safety helmet from height onto a hard surface can also reduce the strength, even if there is no obvious damage. If this happens it should be replaced.

Foot protection

Safety footwear must be worn at all times on site and should have protective toe-caps and a steel mid-sole or other form of protection to protect from puncture injuries (such as standing on a nail).

☑ Some offer better ankle support.

☑ Some offer good grip on slippery surfaces (such as safety trainers), where such a facility is required.

☑ Some offer increased comfort and are more suitable to trades (such as floor layers) who repeatedly kneel and bend their feet.

High-visibility clothing

☑ All staff and visitors on site should wear a high-visibility vest or coat as a minimum.

☑ There are three classes of high-visibility clothing.

– **Class 1 – low visibility** (tabards and waistcoats) suitable for general sites.

– **Class 2 – medium visibility** needed when working on or near A and B class roads or heavily trafficked sites.

– **Class 3 – high visibility** needed when working on or near dual carriageways, motorways or airports.

B 05

Body protection

Protective clothing can be used to protect against the following.

☑ Strong oils and chemicals (for example, cement).

☑ Rough or sharp surfaces.

☑ Ignition and burning (fire retardant).

☑ Extreme cold or heat.

☑ Extreme (wet and windy) weather.

Hearing protection

There are two main types of hearing protection.

☑ Ear defenders or earmuffs.

– These are worn around the shell of the ear and have to be a snug fit to be properly effective.

☑ Earplugs.

– These are inserted into the outer ear.

– Make sure your earplugs are inserted properly. They should not feel loose or fall out.

– Do not reuse disposable earplugs, as this can cause infection.

Eye and face protection

The three main types are shown below.

Safety glasses (low-impact eye protection)

Safety goggles

Face shield

Safety glasses and other forms of low-impact eye protection are not designed for tasks where high-impact eye protection should be worn (such as when using cartridge tools, grinders or disc cutters).

☑ Different types of eye protection protect you against the following.

- Flying debris and objects.
- Chemical splashes.
- Airborne dust.
- Molten metal and sparks.

☑ Eye protection needs to be regularly cleaned and stored to protect it from scratching.

☑ You need to be able to see through your eye protection for you to be able to work safely.

☑ If your eye protection is scratched or mists up then you need a suitable replacement.

 Safety glasses are only classed as low-impact eye protection and will not withstand an impact from flying debris when using grinders, disc cutters, cartridge tools, and so on.

Hand and skin protection

☑ Gloves should be suitable for the hazards and task. Using the correct type of gloves will protect your hands.

☑ If using chemicals the gloves should be impervious (the chemical should not go through the glove onto your hands).

☑ It is important that gloves are regularly cleaned or replaced.

Barrier creams are no substitute for gloves but can offer an extra line of protection. Using hand soap, hand cleaners and after work creams to replace oils lost from your skin will help in prevention.

Never use solvents or spirits to clean your hands. These strip the protective oils from your hands leaving you more prone to attack. 5%-10% of construction workers working with cement, mortar and concrete are affected by dermatitis.

Personal flotation equipment, including lifejackets

☑ If you have to work on, over or near to water there is a risk of drowning and you should be provided with personal flotation equipment (such as a lifejacket). This should be worn properly at all times that you are at risk of falling into the water.

☑ Falling into water wearing your work clothing and boots, or even your tool belt will drag you under or sap your energy quickly, especially in cold or fast moving water.

☑ Self-inflating lifejackets automatically inflate and turn you onto your back, even if you are unconscious, allowing you to breathe.

☑ Other, more basic but equally important equipment (such as life-buoys, life-rings or throwing lines) may also be provided.

☑ Where strong currents or fast flowing water are present there may be a need for other equipment (such as manned rescue boats).

B
05

Types of respiratory protective equipment

To prevent exposure to harmful dust, fibres, fumes and gases, employers must provide you with the correct type of respiratory (breathing) protective equipment (RPE).

The choice of RPE will depend upon the nature of hazard from which the protection is required. In many cases RPE will only protect against one type of hazard (for example dust), although combined protection RPE is also available. Colour coding is used to show what the equipment's filter will protect against. The choice of RPE must be made by an authorised, competent person. The wrong equipment or filter will offer no protection.

As with all PPE you should be told why it is necessary, how and when to wear it, how to keep it clean and store it, and what to do if you have any doubts about its effectiveness or if it gets lost or damaged.

If you are issued with RPE, your employer should arrange for it to be face-fit tested, to ensure it fits and functions correctly.

☑ Where dust cannot be avoided you must wear suitable RPE (masks).

☑ If wearing a mask it should have a BS EN number and/or CE mark printed on it.

☑ Disposable masks should have at least two adjustable straps and may have a flexible nose band to shape around the bridge of your nose.

☑ There should be a good seal between the facepiece and your skin. Facial hair and other items of PPE (such as safety glasses) can interfere with the fit.

Cheap disposable (nuisance) dust masks from DIY stores offer little or no protection and should not be used.

Common types of RPE include disposable filter masks, half and full face respirators with replacement (disposable) filter cartridges.

☑ RPE should have a filter rating **FFP3, FFP2 or FFP1**. The filters can protect against different hazards (such as dusts or vapours).

- **FFP3** will offer the maximum protection. These reduce the dust you breathe in by a factor of 20.
- **FFP2** are good for medium risk. These reduce the amount of dust you breathe in by a factor of 10.
- **FFP1** are suitable for light duty work (such as sweeping up). These reduce the amount of dust you breathe in by a factor of four.

B
05

FFP3 gives a protection factor of 20, meaning that, for every 20 dust particles outside of the mask it is predicted that only one would pass through the filter material.

FFP1 or FFP2 masks are unlikely to give enough protection against hazardous dusts, and should only be used for nuisance dusts. The seal should be tight against your face. Facial hair can reduce the effectiveness of the RPE. You should be clean shaven at the start of each shift to make sure the RPE seals properly against your skin.

The risk assessment or control of substances hazardous to health (COSHH) assessment should say what type of filter is needed.

☑ **If in any doubt – ask. You have the right not to breathe in harmful dusts and fumes.**

☑ **Protect today – breathe easily tomorrow.**

Disposable half mask respirator. (Note the two straps passing above and below the ears)

Half face, face mask. (The colour coded bands on the nosepiece show what the appropriate replacement filter will provide protection against)

06
Asbestos

What your site and employer should do for you

1. Make sure that information about the location of asbestos is made available to the workforce and others who may be affected.

2. Arrange for health surveillance where legislation or policy requires it.

3. Develop suitable control measures to manage your exposure.

4. Provide you with suitable training, relevant to the level of work being carried out.

5. Provide appropriate personal protective equipment (PPE), where required.

6. Provide supervision to make sure the control measures are being used properly.

What you should do for your site and employer

1. Follow any system of work that your employer has in place.

2. Never assume that all of the asbestos located in a building has been found.

3. Make sure that you wear any PPE properly.

4. Stop work, keep away and warn others if you think you have discovered asbestos.

5. Attend health surveillance, when requested by your employer.

Introduction

Asbestos is a harmful substance that continues to kill many people every year. It is the biggest occupational killer in the UK.

The microscopic asbestos fibres are invisible and are easily disturbed.

Breathing in **any** type of asbestos fibre can lead to lung diseases (such as mesothelioma, asbestosis and lung cancer).

 Around 5,000 people die each year as a result of past exposure to asbestos.

Where you will find asbestos

It has been estimated that asbestos was included in over 5,000 construction products in the 1940s to the 1980s. The use of asbestos and asbestos containing materials (ACM) were mainly used in the following.

Asbestos flue

☑ Sprayed coatings to ceilings, columns and beams.

☑ Lagging of boilers, pipework or ducting.

☑ Pipework and boiler gaskets.

☑ Suspended ceiling tiles and floor tiles.

☑ Partitions and ceilings.

☑ Soffit panels and window boards.

☑ Asbestos cement roofing sheets, water tanks and pipes.

☑ Asbestos cement used as permanent formwork.

 Any building constructed before 2000 must, by law, be considered as potentially containing asbestos, and must be subject to an appropriate survey.

Asbestos is often hidden above suspended ceilings and behind walls. Workers should assume that asbestos may still be present, even after a survey has been completed.

If you think that you have discovered or disturbed asbestos, you must make sure of the following.

☑ Stop work immediately.

☑ Warn others nearby to keep away.

☑ Tell your supervisor or employer.

Asbestos surveys

An asbestos survey should be undertaken by a competent person before the work starts. The results of the survey are essential in planning the work. There are two types of asbestos survey.

☑ **Management survey.** To assess how to manage and protect asbestos in an occupied building.

☑ **Refurbishment or demolition survey.** This must be undertaken before any invasive construction work starts. This survey is much more comprehensive than a management survey.

Asbestos can only be correctly identified by getting a sample analysed in a laboratory.

 In the absence of a laboratory report, it must be assumed that the material contains asbestos.

Working with asbestos

Any worker who is due to work in a building that is likely to contain asbestos and whose work may expose them to or bring them into contact with asbestos, must complete a suitable asbestos awareness course before starting work.

Workers may come into contact with asbestos when undertaking maintenance, refurbishment or demolition work, such as the following.

☑ Modifying the structure (partial demolition).

☑ Stripping out.

☑ Installing new plumbing, electrics, windows and soffits, loft insulation, kitchens and bathrooms.

Asbestos warning label

Never attempt to work on asbestos unless you are competent and equipped to do so, and if necessary, licenced.

All work with asbestos requires a written assessment of the risks, appropriate levels of precaution (such as the use of personal protective equipment) and appropriate training.

B
06

Asbestos removal

Projects can be categorised in the following ways.

☑ Licensed asbestos work.

☑ Notifiable non-licensed work.

☑ Non-licensed work.

The removal of high risk asbestos containing materials (such as sprayed asbestos, asbestos lagging and asbestos insulating board (AIB)) must be carried out by a licensed contractor.

The removal of low risk asbestos containing materials (such as asbestos cement products and vinyl floor tiles) would not normally require a licence, providing that the correct precautions were taken (such as wearing the correct respiratory protective equipment). Training must be provided to all employees undertaking this work.

B
06

Damaged asbestos lagging

Labelled encapsulated asbestos

If you are carrying out work with asbestos you must ensure the following.

☑ You understand and follow the written plan of work.

☑ You use the correct respiratory protective equipment (RPE) and personal protective equipment (PPE).

☑ You follow company procedures for the cleaning, maintenance and storage of your RPE and PPE.

☑ You maintain your RPE and PPE in a clean and efficient state, good order and repair.

☑ You use the washing and changing facilities provided.

 You must be given awareness training if you are at risk of encountering or disturbing asbestos whilst carrying out your normal everyday work.

Asbestos

B
06

07

Dust and fumes (Respiratory hazards)

51

Dust and fumes (Respiratory hazards)

What your site and employer should do for you

1. Make sure that respiratory hazards (such as dust, fumes and vapours) are either eliminated or minimised.

2. Provide equipment and systems to make sure that exposures to respiratory hazards are reduced to the lowest level possible.

3. Provide information, instruction and training on the hazards and controls (such as on-tool extraction and wet cutting methods).

4. Issue you with the correct respiratory protective equipment (RPE) needed to protect your health, and train you how to check it, wear it properly, clean it, store it and look after it properly, and tell you what to do if it is damaged or lost.

B 07

What you should do for your site and employer

1. Make sure you know what and how respiratory hazards can damage your long-term health.

2. Use any equipment provided to make the task safer (such as on-tool extraction methods).

3. Follow the safe system of work given for the tasks you are carrying out.

4. Look after and wear your RPE properly, and replace it, including any disposable filters, as necessary.

5. Ask, if in any doubt, and report any changes in your health or problems with protective equipment.

Introduction

Respiratory hazards are substances in the air (such as construction dust) that can be inhaled and can lead to a range of illnesses and diseases. Damage is mainly caused to the lungs and airways, and includes lung cancer and silicosis. However, some respiratory hazards can also result in diseases in other parts of the body, such as the kidneys and liver.

 The Health and Safety Executive estimates that around 600 construction workers die each year from silica-related lung diseases. Much of this exposure is related to activities such as cutting paving slabs, blocks or kerbs.

As well as deaths from respiratory hazards, many more workers suffer chronic, debilitating health conditions (such as occupational asthma) from breathing in hazardous substances on site. Many people are forced to leave the industry due to work-related ill health.

B
07

The effects of exposure to most respiratory hazards are not always immediate. You may go home from work feeling more or less the same each day, not realising that you have been exposed to a substance that may cause problems in the future.

If you are repeatedly exposed to small doses of dust, fumes and vapours they may start to damage your body. The effects of these small doses build up over time. It can take months or even years before symptoms of exposure start to show and become a problem and by then irreversible damage to your health may have occurred.

 At any one time there are far more people off work through occupational ill health than because of work-related accidents.

Exposure to everyday hazards, including things like wood dusts, flux, welding fumes, dusts from slab cutting, asbestos and many more common workplace materials, can cause ill health.

Some dusts and fumes, known as respiratory sensitisers, can cause workers to develop asthma if inhaled.

Breathing in hazardous airborne substances can cause wheezing, coughing, breathlessness, bronchitis and other respiratory diseases, including various types of cancer.

Exposure to solvent vapours can cause acute (immediate) effects as well as chronic (long-term) illness. This means an affected person can suffer headaches, dizziness, unconsciousness and even death if they are exposed to high concentrations of airborne hazardous substances, particularly if exposed in a restricted, poorly ventilated or confined space.

Workers in the construction industry are exposed to many materials and products, some of which are particular respiratory hazards (such as asbestos, cement, stone, silica, lead, MDF, plastics, epoxies and solvents).

Respiratory hazards

The following categories describe the main respiratory hazards that may be encountered on site.

Dust

Dust is produced when solid materials are broken down into finer particles. Dust may be classed as either inhalable dust (larger dust particles that can enter the airway and may be coughed up) and respirable dusts (that go down into and remain in the deep lung). Generally, the finer the particles are, the more hazardous they are, since they can get deeper into the lungs. The most hazardous dust particles are invisible to the naked eye and stay suspended in the air for long periods.

Operative working with dust suppression to reduce airborne dust

☑ **Nuisance dust** has no particular harmful properties but, if inhaled in large enough quantities, can still be harmful and cause breathlessness, wheezing, coughing and irritation.

☑ **Asbestos** fibres in air are responsible for several forms of cancer, including lung cancer and mesothelioma, as well as asbestosis. The microscopic fibres are easily released into the air by disturbing asbestos or asbestos containing materials (ACMs). Asbestos is not easily recognised in materials and is often missed on construction sites. *(For further information refer to Chapter B06 Asbestos.)*

☑ **Silica.** Respirable crystalline silica (RCS) are microscopic particles of silica found in many construction materials (such as paving slabs, blocks and kerbs). Prolonged exposure to silica dust can cause silicosis, lung cancer and other life-changing or life-shortening conditions. Fine silica dust is created when materials are sanded, cut or drilled.

☑ **Lead** is a toxic metal that can cause many ill health effects (such as mental disturbance, effects on the digestive system, and even coma). Breathing in lead dust is only one of the ways that lead can enter the body. It can also enter by inhaling fumes from vapourised lead through absorption and ingestion. In construction, lead can be found in old paint, flashings and roofing materials.

☑ **Wood dust**, created by cutting and sanding, is particularly hazardous, causing a range of health effects, from sensitisation to cancer. Softwood dust is known to cause sensitisation (a form of allergic reaction). Hardwood is a known cancer causing agent (a carcinogen) known to be responsible for lung cancer and cancer of the nasal passages. Medium density fibreboard (MDF) is made from separated softwood fibres, hardwood fibres and glues. It can form a particularly fine dust when cut, which increases the likelihood of dangerous amounts being breathed in.

☑ **Bird and bat droppings**, accumulations of which are common on construction sites, particularly on demolition or redevelopment projects. Droppings often contain a number of bacterial and fungal biological hazards. If disturbed, they can release a hazardous airborne dust that can result in severe respiratory illness (such as psittacosis) that causes pneumonia. If work is to be carried out in an area where pigeons, starlings or bats have been congregating or nesting, the area must be thoroughly decontaminated first, and those carrying out the decontamination must wear suitable respiratory protective equipment (RPE).

Dust is by far the most common hazard on construction sites and in construction work.

Fumes

Fumes are produced by the heating of metals to high temperatures (such as during welding and gas cutting). Fumes are effectively gases that contain tiny metal particles (molecules) that can be inhaled. Metal fume fever is one of the main illnesses caused by breathing in metal fumes. It is caused by inhaling fumes from the welding or hot working of a number of metals, particularly galvanised steel. It is an acute illness, causing flu-like symptoms.

Vehicle exhaust emissions

Personal carbon monoxide alarm

Vehicle exhaust emissions contain many hazardous substances, including toxic gases and particulates. Carbon monoxide (CO) may cause death quickly, particularly where engines are used or their exhaust gases are discharged into confined spaces where high concentrations of CO gas can build up quickly. Sooty particles from diesel engines are very fine, and can penetrate deep into the lung, causing lung cancer. Avoiding the use of engine powered equipment (such as disc cutters and generators) in enclosed spaces, spaces with restricted or poor ventilation and confined spaces will reduce the risk. However, where this cannot be avoided, adequate ventilation must be provided and carbon monoxide gas detectors should be used.

Gases

Gases are chemicals in their gaseous state at room temperature. They mix with the air we breathe, and may be a simple asphyxiant (such as nitrogen) or toxic (such as hydrogen sulphide). Hydrogen sulphide (H_2S) is given off by rotting organic substances (such as sewage and rotting vegetation). It can build up in poorly ventilated or confined spaces (such as sewers, drains, silos and slurry tanks). H_2S smells of rotten eggs and attacks the nerve endings in the nose, disabling them. People think that if they can no longer smell it, the gas has disappeared, but it is still there and has simply disabled the sense of smell. At sufficient concentrations it can cause unconsciousness within a few breaths, and death in a short space of time. Other toxic gases often encountered in construction are carbon dioxide and carbon monoxide, although they usually only reach toxic concentrations when released into confined spaces or restricted spaces with poor ventilation.

B
07

Vapours

Gases and vapours can build up quickly in confined spaces

Vapours are the gaseous state of substances that are liquids at room temperature. (As fumes can be said to be gases, carrying suspended solid particles, vapours can be said to be gases carrying suspended liquid particles.) Vapours usually form when a substance evaporates (for example, the vapour from glue or paint). Solvents are also used for many different construction processes and can release high levels of vapour. Vapours can build up quickly in poorly ventilated or confined spaces and can cause headaches, dizziness, collapse and, in rare cases, death. Many vapours are also highly flammable and can be explosive. Long-term exposure to some solvent vapours can also cause chronic health effects (such as liver and lung damage).

Mists and aerosols

Mists and aerosols are fine droplets of liquid suspended in air. The droplets are often of respirable size, which means that, if inhaled, they can get deep into the lungs. Some examples of hazardous mists and aerosols are listed below.

☑ **Twin pack paints**, used for creating high-quality finishes, usually contain isocyanates, which are powerful respiratory sensitisers, as well as being respiratory irritants. They can cause acute symptoms (such as respiratory irritation and bronchitis), but they can also cause asthma if inhaled over a period of time.

☑ **Legionella** is a common bacteria in the aquatic environment. In spray or mist form this can easily be inhaled, resulting in legionellosis, which is the name for a group of diseases caused by the legionella bacteria. The most commonly known of these diseases is probably legionnaires' disease, which is a potentially fatal form of pneumonia. In construction, water aerosols may arise from dust suppression systems and vehicle washes.

Controlling exposure to hazards

The following simple steps should be taken to protect you from respiratory hazards.

☑ **Avoid creating dust.** Choosing the right equipment or method of work can protect workers' lungs and potentially eliminate the risk altogether. Pre-order sized materials rather than cutting them on site or use a block splitter rather than a disc cutter as this creates less dust and is quicker.

☑ **Stop the dust getting into the air.** If the creation of dust cannot be eliminated then minimising the dust being released should be the priority. This can be done by capturing the dust or dampening down.

Using a water-fed cut-off saw whilst wearing respiratory protection

– **Capturing the dust.** Some materials (such as wood) do not suit the use of water to suppress dusts, so dust extraction should be considered. When your employer purchases or hires tools they should make sure that they have on-tool dust capture (extraction) wherever possible. Cleaning dust from work areas and tools is far better if a vacuum is used rather than sweeping with a brush.

– **Dampening down or wet cutting.** This is the cheapest and most effective way of minimising exposure. Water helps to form a slurry that prevents the majority of dust becoming airborne. Not only does it reduce what is breathed in, but it also has the benefit of less cleaning up afterwards. It is important to keep the flow constant while wet cutting or grinding and to dampen down before clearing up.

B
07

☑ **Wear respiratory protection.** Even the best control measures won't prevent dust generation completely, so RPE must always be worn, even if you are using dust capture (extraction) or wet cutting.

 Refer to Chapter B05 Personal protective equipment for further information about RPE.

B
07

08

Noise and vibration

Noise and vibration

What your site and employer should do for you

1. Make assessments to see if you are exposed to excessive levels of noise or vibration.
2. Develop suitable control measures to manage your exposure to noise.
3. Provide you with sufficient training so you are clear about the hazards from noise and vibration.
4. Provide appropriate hearing protection.
5. Provide supervision to make sure the control measures are being used properly.
6. Arrange for health surveillance where your exposure dictates this is necessary.

B 08

What you should do for your site and employer

1. Make sure you understand the damage that excessive noise and vibration can do to you.
2. Wear your hearing protection when needed.
3. Make sure that you wear your hearing protection properly.
4. Look after your hearing protection and get it replaced if it is lost or damaged.
5. When using hand-held vibrating tools do not exceed the daily safe time limit, if one has been specified.
6. Attend health surveillance, when requested by your employer.

60

Introduction to noise

Noise is sometimes referred to as unwanted sound. Damage caused to your hearing by exposure to noise can be permanent. As well as hearing loss, many workers also suffer from constant ringing or buzzing noises in one or both ears. This is known as tinnitus and there is no cure for it.

Noise-induced hearing loss can build up over time. You may not notice the effects each day, but over a period of time your hearing can get worse from the noise you are exposed to at work. When hearing damage becomes significant you may notice the following.

☑ You start to turn the television up a bit more than you used to.

☑ You struggle to hear conversations or parts of words, particularly when there is background noise (such as in social situations).

There are various sources of noise on a construction site. Many of these are made by hand-held tools and can give high noise exposures because they are close to the user's ears and because of the pitch of the sound they produce.

Other sources of noise could include the following.

☑ Tools that you are using.

☑ Tools that other people are using nearby.

☑ Site equipment (such as generators).

☑ Plant (such as excavators and concrete breakers).

Damage can be caused by continuous noise (such as drills and breakers) and peak noise, usually from impacts (such as from cartridge-operated tools or piling rigs).

As well as causing hearing damage, excessive noise on a construction site can mask other noises (for example, warnings or the sound of vehicles approaching). This creates an additional hazard (such as being struck by site vehicles).

Employer responsibilities

Employers have a legal duty to make sure your hearing is not damaged at work. They must also tell you about the risks from noise and take steps to protect your hearing. They can do this in the following ways.

☑ By selecting and using the quietest equipment available (such as generators with silencing kits fitted).

☑ By planning to do the work using the quietest methods available (such as cutting holes with rotary diamond cutters rather than chain drilling with hammer drills).

☑ By keeping you away from the noisiest activities, wherever possible.

☑ By providing you with personal protective equipment (PPE).

Where the noise levels are not reduced enough using the first three methods above, your employer should provide you with hearing protection to further reduce your exposure.

B
08

Hearing protection

There are two main types of hearing protection, each has its own advantages and disadvantages.

 Induction briefings, site rules and signage will tell you where you should wear hearing protection. Make sure you wear it, where and when instructed to do so.

B
08

Earplugs

☑ These can be foam plugs, which may also be mounted to a band or cord.

☑ They must be fitted correctly so that they work properly, otherwise they have very little effect.

☑ They must be fitted with clean hands, otherwise dirt can get into the ears and cause infection and other problems.

☑ You should be shown how to fit earplugs properly.

Foam earplugs worn incorrectly

Foam earplugs worn correctly

Hearing defenders (earmuffs)

☑ These cover the outer shell of the ear and need to make a tight seal against the head to work properly.

☑ They do not provide as much protection when worn over long hair or glasses.

☑ They should be stored properly so they don't get dirty or damaged.

☑ They must be kept clean and be cleaned after use, or they can become unhygienic.

☑ They can get hot and sweaty in hot weather, and can be uncomfortable to wear for long periods.

 Whichever type of hearing protection you use, it must be worn all the time that you are exposed to the upper action noise level. Even short periods of not wearing protection has a huge effect on your daily exposure.

Noise action levels

The daily exposure level is the amount of noise encountered over an assumed eight hour working day. The Noise at Work Regulations give two action levels that are the daily exposure levels at which your employer must take action. If the noise is above a certain level, the amount of time you are exposed to the noise must be reduced in line with this. The issue and wearing of PPE should always be considered as a last resort.

☑ **Lower exposure action level.** At identified (or predicted) noise levels of 80 dB(A) your employer should identify the noise hazard area (by the use of signage) and make sure that appropriate hearing protection is available. These are often called advisory hearing protection zones.

☑ **Upper exposure action level.** At identified (or predicted) noise levels of 85 dB(A) your employer should identify the noise hazard area (by the use of signage), provide suitable hearing protection, and make sure it is used correctly. These areas are often called mandated or compulsory hearing protection zones.

B
08

If you are exposed to the upper exposure action level your employer must put in place a hearing protection programme, which should include health surveillance.

Your employer can insist on the use of hearing protection at any time and/or at any noise level, but in doing so they must make sure that the compulsory use of hearing protection does not increase or affect other risks.

 If you have to raise your voice to be heard by someone two metres away from you, then the noise level is in the range of 80 dB(A). If you have to raise your voice to be heard by someone who is one metre away, then the noise level is likely to be in the range of 85 dB(A).

A hand tool giving 95 dB(A) at your ear would result in you reaching the 80 db(A) action level in just 15 minutes, and the 85 dB(A) action level in under an hour.

A petrol cut-off saw giving 105 dB(A) at your ear would result in you reaching the 80 dB(A) action level in under two minutes, and the 85 dB(A) action level in around five minutes.

Introduction to vibration

Exposure to vibration can have serious health effects. Vibration from hand-held tools can cause hand-arm vibration syndrome (HAVS), which affects many workers in the construction industry. Whole-body vibration (WBV) can also occur in the construction industry and may affect drivers of construction vehicles, often resulting in back injury.

HAVS is a range of conditions caused by exposure to vibration through the hands. The condition is permanent and disabling. The damage being done affects the nerves, blood vessels, muscles, bones and other tissues of the hands and arms. Symptoms within the hands often include the following.

☑ Tingling.

☑ Numbness.

☑ Loss of sensation.

☑ Loss of manual dexterity.

☑ Painful throbbing.

☑ Extreme burning in the fingers and hands, especially after they have been exposed to the cold or become wet.

There may also be muscle fatigue and loss of grip strength, as well as conditions such as carpal tunnel syndrome and tennis elbow.

B 08

A common symptom of HAVS is finger blanching. This appears as discolouration of the fingers, which may be temporary at first, but with longer exposure can become permanent.

People with HAVS often have problems with everyday tasks (such as fastening buttons). It is also painful, particularly when the hands are cold or damp.

Finger blanching caused by vibration

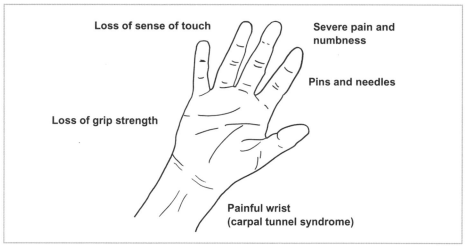

Vibration related damage to the hands

 If you are diagnosed with HAVS you must inform your employer as they have a legal duty to report this to the Health and Safety Executive (HSE).

Equipment that can cause HAVS

HAVS is caused by the use of hand-held equipment, that generates high levels of vibration. Typical equipment that produces enough vibration to cause HAVS includes the following.

☑ Compressed air breakers, pneumatic drills, concrete pokers and scabblers.

☑ Hand-held drills, including hammer drills and rock drills.

☑ Disc cutters, angle grinders and wall chasers.

☑ Sanders, circular saws and planers.

☑ Plate compactors and strimmers.

Your chance of getting HAVS depends on the vibration dose you receive each day. The dose is a combination of the amount of vibration produced by the tool and the length of time it is used for each day. A common way of managing the risk from vibration in the construction industry is by limiting the daily dose of workers (the amount of time they spend using vibrating tools).

B
08

Managing vibration risks

Your employer has a duty to make sure that you are not exposed to levels of vibration that can cause damage your health. They must make sure of the following.

☑ Your risk of exposure to vibration is assessed.

☑ Put the following measures in place to control vibration.

– Buy equipment that generates the lowest levels of vibration.

– Choose work methods that avoid exposing workers to vibration, such as the use of machine mounted rather than hand-held breakers.

– Make sure that equipment is well-maintained and attachments (such as bits and discs) are not excessively worn.

– Limit the time you use vibrating equipment so that you do not receive a potentially damaging vibration dose.

☑ Give you information and training so that you know the risks from vibration.

☑ Start health surveillance if you are exposed to significant levels of vibration.

Reducing vibration risks

Although your employer has a duty to protect your health, there are things that **you** can do to reduce your risk of developing HAVS.

☑ Be aware of the usage limits (trigger time limits) for vibrating tools, and make sure you do not exceed them.

☑ Relax your grip and let the tool do the work. Applying too much force or gripping too tightly results in more vibration being transmitted to the hands.

☑ Take regular breaks when using vibrating tools, and during those breaks exercise your fingers to improve the blood supply.

☑ Keep your hands warm – cold hands are more prone to damage from vibration.

Remember the following.

☑ Smokers are more likely to get HAVS than non-smokers (as smoking reduces circulation).

☑ Anti-vibration gloves are not very effective (although gloves may generally be useful in keeping the hands warm).

 The damage caused by exposure to excessive levels of vibration is permanent, debilitating and can affect your personal life and could end your career.

B
08

09

Hazardous substances

What your site and employer should do for you

1. Assess the risks of using a substance.

2. Use a less hazardous substance where possible.

3. Store and dispose of the substances correctly.

4. Control exposure by providing engineering methods (separation, insulation, isolation, local exhaust ventilation) and the use of safe systems of work.

5. Provide information and training on the hazards, risks and controls.

6. Monitor the work and the workplace to make sure the controls are effective and provide health surveillance if needed.

What you should do for your site and employer

1. Fully understand the hazards of using the substance.

2. Follow the safe system of work/controls (control of substances hazardous to health (COSHH) assessment).

3. Store, dispense and dispose of the substance correctly.

4. Wear the correct personal protective equipment (PPE).

5. Report any incident or spill to your supervisor or site management.

6. Attend health surveillance sessions, where necessary.

B
09

Introduction

A hazardous substance can be described in the following ways.

☑ Any substance (solid, liquid, gas, dust, fibre, fume, vapour, spray or mist) that could harm your health (including things such as solvents, cement and asbestos).

☑ Any dust, fibre or fume given off by a work process.

☑ Any substance that could harm the environment.

How hazardous substances can affect your health

☑ **Immediate (acute)** – for example, burns to the skin from acids or chemicals.

☑ **Long-term (chronic)** – for example, developing cancer from asbestos exposure.

☑ **Disease** – for example, through contact with contaminated soil or water.

☑ **Sensitising** – over a period of time you start having more serious allergic reactions to a lower level or less exposure to the substance, and/or a quicker reaction after an exposure.

B
09

How hazardous substances can get into your body (routes of entry)

☑ **Inhalation** – breathing in dust, fumes, vapours and fibres.

☑ **Absorption** – contact with your skin.

☑ **Ingestion** – being swallowed or eaten (usually from holding food or smoking with dirty hands).

☑ **Injection** – needles, sharps or high pressure (such as water jetting) or open sores/wounds in your body.

What your employer should be doing

Under the Control of Substances Hazardous to Health (COSHH) Regulations employers should undertake the following.

☑ Read and understand the manufacturer's information on the substance.

☑ Carry out a risk assessment on how and where it is to be used.

☑ Use a less hazardous substance if available.

☑ Put in place measures to prevent or control any exposure.

☑ Make sure you know the controls.

☑ Monitor to make sure the controls are effective.

 Some hazardous substances, such as those created by work processes (for example, fumes from welding or dust from cutting and sanding) do not have warning labels, as these are created by the work. Your employer has a legal duty to assess these hazards and complete a COSHH assessment in respect of the work, as part of the safe system of work.

If you are exposed to a workplace hazard your employer may ask you to attend regular health surveillance sessions, which you have a duty to attend.

 Health surveillance **is a system of ongoing health checks to detect possible ill health effects at an early stage.**

Employers can then introduce better controls to prevent any ill health effects from getting worse.

Identifying hazardous substances

B
09

The packaging or container of hazardous substances will carry one or more symbol, to indicate its hazardous properties. Globally harmonised and internationally recognised pictographs were introduced in 2009. These are similar to the European Union symbols they replaced, but they are a different colour and shape. Some of the new pictographs are shown in the table below.

Globally harmonised pictograms

	Toxic (can be fatal) if swallowed or inhaled.		Hazardous to the environment and aquatic life.
	Contains gases under pressure. May explode if heated and can cause burns.		Oxidising gases, liquids and solids. May cause or intensify fire.
	Harmful skin, eye or respiratory irritation. May cause an allergic reaction, drowsiness or breathing difficulties.		Damage to organs and may cause serious longer-term health hazards (such as carcinogenicity and respiratory sensitisation).
	Flammable gases, liquids, solids and aerosols. Heating may cause a fire.		Corrosive and can cause severe skin damage or burns.
	Heating may cause an explosion.		

 If you find a substance in a container with no label, make sure that no-one else can come into contact with it and report it to your supervisor.

Disposal of hazardous substances

Hazardous substances can contaminate land, drains, sewers, rivers and the air.

They should **never** be mixed with general (non-hazardous) waste, or poured down drains or sinks, onto the ground, or buried, burnt or fly tipped.

 Your site or employer should have a procedure to dispose of hazardous waste, including empty or part-used containers.

Highly flammable liquids

Highly flammable liquids (HFLs), such as thinners, solvents, petrol and adhesives, can be easily ignited, catch fire and burn fiercely.

They can be identified by this symbol.

If you have to use HFLs you must make sure of the following.

☑ Check there are no naked flames or other sources of ignition nearby.

☑ Only take the amount you need for your immediate needs.

☑ Always follow the storage procedures.

☑ Have the correct fire extinguisher at hand.

 If a fire extinguisher is needed for hot-work activities it must be one specific for the work activity and the workplace. It should be issued or approved by the person authorising the hot work and you should be trained to use it. Fire extinguishers should not be taken from fire points to cover hot works, no matter how close the fire point is or how short the hot work will be.

Liquid petroleum gas

Liquid petroleum gas (LPG) are highly flammable gases held under high pressure to liquefy them. They will readily evaporate if released from the pressure vessel (cylinder). Their gases are heavier than air so will sink into excavations, basements, drains, and so on.

LPG cylinders must be stored upright in a well-ventilated area and in a secure cage.

There are separate regulations covering the safe carriage of LPG cylinders in vehicles.

LPG has a distinctive smell. If you think there might be a leak make sure of the following.

☑ Others are warned to evacuate the area.

☑ Carry out the following only if it is safe to do so.
  – Turn the cylinder supply valve off.
  – Open doors and windows.
  – Eliminate any source of ignition. **Do not** allow the switching (on or off) of electrical apparatus.

☑ It is reported immediately.

B
09

Hazardous substances

 Gas from a leaking LPG cylinder can expand to 250 times the cylinder's volume. It can catch fire at some distance from the original leak and flash (burn) back to the source of the leak.

B
09

10

Manual handling

What your site and employer should do for you

1. Reduce the need for planning delivery, off-loading and distribution of your materials and equipment to avoid unnecessary carrying and lifting.

2. Identify work activities that pose a manual handling risk.

3. Identify the risks to your health from the manual handling of any load.

4. Ask you how you would do the manual handling task (consultation).

5. If the manual handling task has to be done provide the equipment and a safe method of work to minimise any risk of injury.

6. Provide any necessary equipment and training.

7. Provide slip/trip free access routes and adequate lighting levels.

What you should do for your site and employer

1. Follow the safe system of work.

2. Use lifting aids and equipment safely.

3. Co-operate with your employer. If in doubt, ask for advice.

4. Make sure your activities do not put others at risk.

B 10

Introduction

 Manual handling is the moving of any load by bodily force, including lifting, putting down, pushing, pulling or carrying.

Manual handling includes the following.

☑ Repetitive body movements (twisting and turning).

☑ Horizontal movement (pushing and pulling).

☑ Lifting, carrying and lowering of loads and materials.

Using suitable manual handling aids (such as wheel barrows, sack trucks and brick hoists) can reduce the risk of manual handling injuries, which are the construction industry's biggest cause of ill health.

Every year an estimated 900,000 working days are lost due to handling injuries.

Your back is strong but not as strong as you believe it is. **Repeated** twisting, straining and incorrect lifting techniques can, over time, lead to injury.

Manual handling injuries resulting from unsafe or incorrect manual handling can affect the following parts of your body.

☑ Whole body.

☑ Arms.

☑ Back.

☑ Hands.

☑ Shoulders.

☑ Feet and ankles.

Back injuries are most common but hernias, ruptures, sprains and strains are all conditions that can result from manual handling.

Your employer has a legal duty to avoid any manual handling activity that will harm you.

Poor posture (such as slouching on the settee, sleeping on a poor supporting mattress, and sitting in a driving position that twists or doesn't support your spine) can all add to the problem.

Manual handling assessment

Where the workplace assessment shows potential risks to the health of employees from the manual handling of loads, the employer must develop a safe system of work that avoids those risks. This requires attention to four main things.

☑ **Task**. What has to be achieved and by who and when?

☑ **Individual**. Are they male or female, large or small in stature and frame, what is their age and do they have any health issues or injuries?

☑ **Load**. Is it too heavy to lift, can it be broken down into smaller loads, or can two people lift it?

☑ **Environment**. What hazards are there on the route? For example, are there slippery or uneven floors, slopes, steps or narrow passages?

You can remember these four aspects by use of the acronym TILE.

B
10

Task

☑ Can manual handling be avoided completely?

☑ Does the task involve repetitive lifting?

☑ Does the task involve repetitive twisting?

☑ Can the distance a load has to be moved be reduced? (Get it delivered or moved nearer).

☑ Can lifting aids be used (for example a wheelbarrow, trolley or vacuum lifters)?

☑ How and from what height is the load to be lifted or lowered?

☑ Will it be necessary to over reach or stretch to lift or put down the load?

Individual

☑ Will they need specialist manual handling training or training in any technique needed to use the equipment?

☑ Are they male or female, tall or small, young or old?

☑ Are there any earlier injuries or health conditions?

Load

☑ Can the load be split down into smaller loads?

☑ Can it be moved by two (or more) people?

☑ Is the weight and centre of gravity of the load known?

☑ Is it hot, cold, wet or greasy?

☑ Can it be gripped easily or are there adequate and suitable handholds?

Environment

☑ Is the floor or ground free from slip or trip hazards?

☑ Does the load need to be carried up steps or stairs?

☑ Are there any space constraints?

☑ Is the level of lighting adequate?

Team lifting

If the load is large, heavy or awkward get assistance, preferably from someone of about the same size and build as yourself to help maintain the balance of the load during lifting. Team lifting should only be carried out with people of similar capabilities who have been trained to carry out team lifting.

 The only way to avoid manual handling is to use mechanical handling equipment (such as cranes, forklifts, goods hoists and jacks).

B
10

Lifting and handling

Good practice method of lifting (kinetic method)

| (1) Bend at the knees | (2) Grasp the load | (3) Lift, using the legs | (4) Carry the load |

B
10

Good practice method for lifting and placing a load

Use your body wisely (kinetic method)

☑ Let your leg and thigh muscles do the work.

☑ Try to maintain the natural curve of your spine and relax your muscles.

☑ Avoid flexing your back any further once you have started to lift.

☑ Do not snatch the load as you lift.

☑ Avoid leaning sideways or twisting your back, especially when your back is bent.

B
10

11

Safety signs

What your site and employer should do for you

1. Provide signs that are suitable for the hazard or risk.

2. Make sure that safety signs follow standard designs in respect of shape, colour and the use of pictograms.

3. Display any safety sign identified as being needed in your safe system of work.

4. Maintain signs and make sure they are clearly visible.

5. Remove signs if they are no longer needed.

What you should do for your site and employer

1. Understand what signs and signals mean.

2. Follow the instruction or direction on any sign or signal.

3. Do not vandalise or remove any sign.

4. Report any damaged or missing signs.

5. Speak to your supervisor if you are confused by a sign, there seem to be too many signs or your work area needs extra signage.

C
11

Mandatory signs – must do

*General mandatory sign
(to be accompanied where
necessary by another sign)*

*Safety harness must
be worn*

*Safety helmet must
be worn*

*Protective eyewear must
be worn*

*Safety boots or safety
shoes must be worn*

*Safety gloves must
be worn*

**C
11**

Prohibition signs – must not do

No smoking

No naked flames

No access for pedestrians

*Do not extinguish with
water*

Not drinkable

No mobile phones

Warning signs

Combustible or flammable material

Explosive material

Toxic material

Corrosive material

Radioactive material

Overhead load

Industrial vehicles operating

High voltage

*General warning sign
(to be accompanied where
necessary by another sign)*

Emergency escape and first aid signs – safe conditions

Emergency escape route signs

First aid signs

First aid   *Emergency eyewash*   *Emergency shower*

Fire-fighting signs

Fire hose reel   *Fire ladder*   *Fire-fighting equipment*

Fire emergency telephone   *Fire extinguisher*   *Fire alarm call point*

C
11

83

C
11

12

Fire prevention and control

What your site and employer should do for you

1. Undertake a fire risk assessment and inform you of actions to take in the event of an emergency.

2. Provide, maintain and test fire detection and fire-fighting equipment. Keep escape routes and fire exits clear of all obstructions.

3. Provide a secure storage place for the storage of all gas cylinders and flammable liquids and materials.

4. Display a fire action plan that details fire escape routes and fire assembly points.

5. Have a system to control hot work, (such as a hot-work permit).

6. Provide means to make sure rubbish and waste do not build up.

What you should do for your site and employer

1. Know what to do, and how to raise the alarm, if there is a fire.

2. Store materials and fuels in designated areas.

3. Keep exit routes and fire points clear at all times.

4. Practise good housekeeping and clear up your waste.

5. Get a hot-work permit whenever you might create sparks, heat or flames.

6. Report anything you feel could be a fire risk (such as signs of arson).

C
12

Introduction

Fire kills about 260 people every year in the UK and injures many more. On construction, demolition or refurbishment sites there can be a high risk of fire. Depending on the stage of the project, smoke and fire can spread rapidly.

Fire

How fire starts

For fire to start there must be three elements (the fire triangle).

☑ Heat or ignition (such as a spark).

☑ Fuel (something flammable).

☑ Oxygen (air).

Fighting fire

The fire triangle

Fire feeds on fuel and oxygen. Fire-fighting equipment works by removing the following aspects.

☑ The heat or ignition source (cooling with water).

☑ The fuel (starving, for example, by turning off the gas supply).

☑ The oxygen (smothering with foam or a fire blanket).

A fire can start more easily than it can be stopped

C 12

☑ **Boiling point is the temperature a liquid must reach before it will start to release its vapours.**

☑ **Flashpoint is the temperature a liquid must reach for sufficient vapours to exist and there to be a *flash of flame* when an ignition source is introduced (but insufficient vapours to support continued combustion (burning)).**

☑ **Ignition point is the temperature at which a substance gives off enough vapour to allow for continuous combustion (burning), even though the original ignition source is removed.**

Emergency procedures

Your employer will tell you the following information at the site induction.

☑ Where to go in the event of a fire and how to get there safely.

☑ How to raise the alarm.

☑ How to call the emergency services.

☑ Where you can smoke on site (if smoking is allowed).

☑ When the fire alarms are tested.

☑ Who is trained to use fire-fighting equipment.

☑ Who the fire wardens and marshals are.

☑ Who to report signs of arson and break-ins to.

Know what to do in the event of an emergency

C 12

The emergency escape routes may change during the project, so you will need to familiarise yourself with any new routes.

Hot works

Hot work can be any work where heat, sparks or naked flames are produced (such as welding, grinding or soldering).

If you are undertaking hot works you must work in accordance with the site rules for hot works. This often means obtaining a hot-work permit from your supervisor or site management.

What a hot-work permit will tell you

☑ What you must do before you start and when you can start work.

☑ How to prevent sparks, heat and flames from spreading.

☑ Which type of fire extinguisher you should have available.

☑ The site rules about maintaining a fire watch and for how long after the end of the hot works the fire watch must be maintained.

☑ When you must stop.

☑ When you must go back and check the area (one or two hours after hot work ends).

You should be informed of fire safety and evacuation procedures during your site induction (for example, means of raising the alarm, what the fire alarm will sound like, and the location of fire and assembly points).

If you hear the fire alarm you must stop work and go to the fire assembly point immediately.

Portable fire extinguishers

When using portable fire extinguishers it is vital that everyone is vigilant and any hot work is controlled. The table below shows the types of portable fire extinguishers and what to use them on.

Extinguishing medium	Colour of panel	Where not to use
Water: for wood, paper, textile and solid material fires	Red	Do not use on liquid, electrical or metal fires
Foam: for liquid fires	Cream	Do not use on electrical or metal fires
Powder: for liquid and electrical fires	Blue	Do not use on metal fires
Carbon dioxide: for liquid and electrical fires	Black	Do not use on metal fires
Wet chemical: for wood, paper, textile, cooking oil and solid material fires	Yellow	Do not use on liquid, gas or electrical fires

Note: dry powder extinguishers may be provided as well as or substituted for water, foam or carbon dioxide extinguishers. Extinguishers used to control Class B fires (flammable liquids) will not work on Class F fires (cooking oils) because of the high temperatures produced – where the term 'electrical' is used it should be read as 'fires involving electricity or electrical equipment'.

 All mobile plant must be fitted with an appropriate fire extinguisher.

Highly flammable liquids and gases

Highly flammable liquids are those that can be ignited at temperatures below 32°C.

When using these you must only get out the amount you need for the day and the liquids must be kept in a closed container. You should not work with these near naked flames or sparks. Any spillages must be cleared up immediately.

Examples of highly flammable liquids include the following.

☑ Petrol.

☑ Thinners.

☑ Solvents.

☑ Adhesives.

205-litre diesel drum

Compressed gas must be stored in an upright position when being used, transported or stored.

Use appropriate storage

Burning waste is not allowed on site, unless the site has a permit to do so.

C
12

13

Electrical safety, tools and equipment

Electrical safety, tools and equipment

What your site and employer should do for you

1. Isolate and protect from main, underground and overhead supplies.

2. Provide safe, temporary electrics and safety lighting.

3. Provide the right tools, equipment and personal protective equipment (PPE) for the job.

4. Provide information and training so you know how to use the tools and equipment safely.

5. Make sure electrical installations, tools and equipment are inspected and maintained.

What you should do for your site and employer

1. Only use electrical tools or equipment, as selected for you by your employer, in accordance with your safe system of work.

2. Only use tools and equipment if you have had the correct training, and after carrying out the pre-use checks.

3. Use the correct equipment and PPE.

4. Report any damage or faults.

C
13

Introduction to electricity

You can't see it. You can't smell it. It is dangerous and it can kill.

☑ There is no visible way of knowing for sure if a cable or wires are live.

☑ The temporary nature of site electrical distribution systems and the possibility of them being damaged are all the more reason to be careful with electricity.

☑ If there are exposed cables or wires near where you are working, assume they are live and report them.

Electrical voltages

Battery power

☑ Battery-powered tools are by far the safest option.

☑ The severity of any electric shock will be much lower.

☑ There are no trailing leads.

☑ A lot of sites now provide secure battery charging lockers.

C
13

110 volt – yellow

☑ Electrical tools should ideally be a maximum of 110 volt or battery operated on construction sites.

☑ The standard colour code for 110 volt equipment is yellow.

☑ The 110 volt system means you would only get a 55 volt shock.

☑ You would feel an electric shock from faulty 110 volt equipment but no lasting damage should be done.

230 volt – blue

☑ Domestic voltage or mains power is 230 volts.

☑ It is commonly used for generators and electrical distribution.

☑ The standard colour for 230 volt outdoor use is blue.

☑ If a 230 volt cable is damaged, or you can touch the wires that make up the cable you will get a severe or even fatal electric shock.

☑ 230 volt tools are not allowed on most sites.

400 volt – red

☑ The standard colour for 400 volt is red.

☑ It is for equipment needing a lot of power (such as a tower crane).

 Electricity can kill. If in doubt, stop work and report any concerns to your supervisor.

Using extension leads and cables

☑ Always fully unwind extension cables and reels.

☑ A part unwound cable can overheat, melt and catch fire.

☑ Where possible, route cables or leads overhead.

☑ Cables on the floor are trip hazards.

☑ Use protective ramps to protect cables from being run over if they need to be routed at floor level.

☑ Don't route cables across puddles or waterlogged ground.

☑ Get a transformer moved rather than using several leads joined together.

Electrical hazards

☑ There may be overhead power lines on site, which are only completely safe if isolated by a competent and authorised person.

☑ People have been electrocuted and killed when items (such as ladders, towers or mobile plant) accidently touch or come close to live or charged overhead power lines.

☑ Burns, scorch marks or burning odours indicate an electrical fault.

☑ Damaged leads and cables, even if it is just the outer sheathing, must be taken out of use.

☑ If you see smoke from a power tool, switch it off and take it out of use.

☑ If a fuse blows, it means that there is a fault. Switch off and disconnect the equipment and report it to your manager. Do not try to do any repairs (even changing a fuse), unless you are trained, competent and authorised to do so.

Protection devices

☑ Residual current devices (RCDs) work by cutting the power quickly if there is a fault.

☑ Portable RCDs fit between the plug and the socket.

☑ They must be kept free of moisture and dirt and protected against vibration and mechanical damage.

☑ Your site rules may require you to use a RCD with any 230 volt tool.

☑ Portable RCDs should have a combined inspection and test before first use and then every month.

☑ Portable RCD units should have a mechanical (trip) test before each use by pressing the test/trip button.

 Electricity travels at the speed of light – more than 186,000 miles per second. We don't!

Portable appliance testing

☑ HSE guidance recommends that tools, leads and equipment should be tested every three months if used on site.

☑ If used, the portable appliance testing (PAT) label will tell you when the next safety check is due.

Introduction to hand-held tools and equipment

Many types of power tools and hand tools are used in the construction industry. Thousands of injuries happen because of mis-use and abuse of hand-held tools and equipment.

Moving parts, rotating blades and drill bits can cause serious injury in an instant, as can non-powered hand tools (such as handsaws, trimming knives and hammers).

Because they are used regularly you can become complacent to the hazards and risks.

Noise and vibration from using hand-held tools and equipment can pose a serious risk to health, as can the dust created by drilling and chipping operations. The effects may not be felt right away, and can build up and get worse over time.

Refer to Chapter B08 Noise and vibration for further information.

C
13

Safe methods of working

Competence

To operate powered hand tools and equipment you must be competent. To be competent you will have undergone training to give you the knowledge, understanding and skills required to use tools safely and work in safety.

☑ You need knowledge of the tool and the hazards associated with its use.

☑ You must have an understanding of the environment the tool is to be used in and its limitations.

☑ You must be trained and authorised to use certain tools, abrasive wheels and grinding discs, for example.

☑ You need experience gained by using the tool.

Before using any tool or equipment

☑ Check it is the right tool for the job.

☑ Carry out a pre-use inspection and check.

☑ Make sure it has been maintained and is safe to use.

☑ If you are unsure – ask!

The correct tools, equipment and PPE needed should be listed in the method statement and/or safe system of work for the task.

Guards and safety features

☑ Make sure all guards or other safety features (such as emergency stops) are in place and working properly.

☑ Make sure all guards or other safety features are properly adjusted to minimise any gap between the work piece and any moving part.

☑ Always use tools, plant and equipment properly, and in line with your training.

☑ Always isolate the power and remove the plug from the socket when changing bits, blades, or adjusting guards on power tools.

☑ Never carry out any makeshift repairs or modifications. This includes electrical repairs (for example, changing a fuse) unless you are trained, competent and authorised to do so.

Protect yourself

C 13

☑ Keep hands away from moving parts.

☑ Avoid loose clothing, and make sure power leads don't get entangled in moving parts, which can cause serious injury.

☑ Wear eye protection suitable for the task to be carried out and the tool.

☑ You may need to wear suitable hearing protection, due to the noise level of most power tools.

☑ Make sure that you do not exceed the daily safe vibration exposure limits when using vibrating tools. Information about the vibration level of a tool should be included in the method statement and/or safe system of work for the task.

Types of hand-held equipment

Petrol-driven hand tools

☑ Petrol must be kept in approved containers, and never stored at the location of the work being carried out.

☑ Refuelling should only take place at the designated, authorised refuelling point. You will be briefed on this at site induction.

☑ Designated areas should be well-lit, well-ventilated and use a dispensing nozzle or funnel.

☑ Do not refuel when the engine is running or when any parts are still hot.

☑ Do not smoke while you are refuelling, or at the refuelling point.

Exhaust fumes are toxic and must not be allowed to accumulate in enclosed, poorly ventilated or confined spaces. Do not use petrol, diesel or LPG driven tools in a confined space or area with poor ventilation unless you have specific authority and a written safe system of work for the task. The safe system of work should include forced air ventilation and continuous gas monitoring.

Abrasive wheels and diamond blades

☑ The following are common types of machine.

- Petrol cut off saws (disc cutters).
- Angle grinders.
- Tile cutters.
- Masonry bench saws.
- Wall chasers and floor saws.

Wear the appropriate PPE and ensure the guards are properly set

Abrasive wheels and diamond blades can burst, shatter or suffer high speed segment loss (fragmentation) in the following situations.

☑ If the blade or disc used is not the correct type.

☑ If the blade or disc is not fitted correctly.

☑ If the machine is not used correctly.

☑ Failure, shattering or fragmentation of a disc or blade can result in serious personal injury.

☑ You must be trained, competent and authorised to change or mount a wheel or blade.

☑ The speed of the wheel or blade must match the machine speed.

☑ Only cut material the wheel or blade is made for.

☑ Diamond blades can fail in lots of different ways if misused.

C
13

☑ Diamond blade manufacturers supply free inspection and fault-finding guides.

High-impact eye protection must be worn when you are using abrasive wheels, disc cutters, cut-off saws or diamond blade cutters.

 Using a concrete diamond blade on tarmac can seriously weaken the blade. The result is that the blade will fragment (disintegrate) and nail-sized segments can fly off at high speed (approximately 180 mph).

Electrical hand tools

Ideally all electrical hand tools used on site should be battery operated or 110 volts.

Before every use you should carry out a visual inspection.

☑ **Check the power lead.** Check for signs of damage where it enters the tool. Look to see if the cable's internal wires are visible. Are there signs of charring, has the cable been pulled or used to carry the tool, or is the outer insulation of the cable damaged?

☑ **Check the plug.** Is it damaged in any way? Does the plug show signs of charring, can you see the internal wires of the cable, is there a legible PAT label?

☑ **Check the socket.** Is it damaged in any way? Does it show signs of charring, is a RCD fitted? If a RCD is not fitted, test and fit a portable RCD unit before connecting the plug to the socket.

☑ You must switch off, disconnect and secure the plug before carrying out any adjustments so that the power cannot be reconnected by accident.

Cartridge-operated tools

Poor practice and lack of concentration can lead to injuries

☑ These work like a gun by firing an explosive charge.

☑ They are used to fire fixings into solid surfaces (such as concrete or steel columns).

☑ They are very dangerous, especially in untrained hands.

☑ You must be specifically trained and authorised to use a cartridge-operated tool.

☑ Suitable high-impact eye protection and hearing protection must be worn.

☑ An exclusion zone must be in place during fixing operations.

☑ Cartridge-operated tools need to be inspected, cleaned and lubricated regularly.

Compressed gas tools (nail guns)

Nail guns are similar to cartridge-operated tools but they use a gas canister or battery as the energy (fuel) source.

☑ They should only be used by trained, competent and authorised persons.

☑ High-impact eye protection must be worn. Eye protection must be replaced if it is scratched or damaged.

☑ Remove the battery, fuel cell and remaining nails before clearing a blockage or cleaning.

☑ They need to be inspected, cleaned and lubricated regularly.

☑ Fuel cells or canisters must be disposed of correctly.

☑ Tool manufacturers often offer free, on-site training.

C
13

Compressed air-powered tools

☑ Compressed air tools are attached to a compressor using air hoses.

☑ Tools include heavy duty breakers, soil picks, concrete scabblers and pokers.

☑ High pressure air hoses can cause serious injury if they break away from the compressor or tool. **Whip checks** should be used on every hose joint to prevent this.

☑ Always check hose fittings are tight and secure before use.

Whip checks should be used on certain types of hose joint

Chainsaws

☑ Chainsaws can inflict serious injuries including amputation.

☑ The main hazard is that they have a fully exposed cutting chain.

☑ Chainsaws can kick back (uncontrollably kick upwards towards the operator with the chain running).

☑ You must be fully trained, competent and authorised and wearing full chainsaw protective body clothing and head protection.

C
13

Non-powered hand tools

☑ These may seem low risk, but are responsible for many injuries.

☑ They need to be well maintained and regularly inspected.

☑ Well used chisels and bolsters can form 'mushroom heads'. When they are struck fragments can fly into the air and into the eye.

☑ Loose handles, blunt blades and worn parts all pose a hazard.

Lasers

☑ If used correctly lasers should not pose a health hazard.

☑ A rotating laser means it is difficult to look directly at the beam for more than an instant.

☑ Static lasers (such as pipe lasers) pose more of a risk.

☑ Exclusion zones and warning signs must be in place if high-powered lasers are being used.

 Always follow the manufacturer's instructions when using any tool or equipment.

C
13

14

Site transport safety

What your site and employer should do for you

1. Provide safe methods for deliveries, unloading and parking.

2. Provide separate routes for pedestrians and vehicles.

3. Provide signage, markings, barriers and lighting.

4. Arrange one-way systems and speed limits, and ban or control reversing.

5. Explain the site traffic rules to you at induction.

What you should do for your site and employer

1. Follow all signs and speed limits.

2. Only use designated walking routes.

3. Do not bring any vehicle onto site unless your supervisor has authorised you to do so.

4. Do not move or operate plant if you are not trained and have not been authorised to do so.

5. Always wear your high-visibility clothing.

6. Report any plant movement you think is unsafe or too close to your work.

C
14

Introduction

The movement of mobile-operated plant and vehicles causes many accidents and serious injuries on sites every year. The accidents involve not only the operator but people working close by or just walking past.

Mobile plant and site vehicles

The term *mobile plant* covers all mobile plant and site vehicles that can move either under their own power or by being towed. Some examples are listed below.

- ☑ Dumpers.
- ☑ Excavators.
- ☑ Telehandlers and forklifts.
- ☑ Mobile cranes and piling rigs.
- ☑ HGVs, lorries and delivery wagons.
- ☑ Vans and cars.
- ☑ Road rollers, including pedestrian-operated rollers.

The term *operator* is used to describe anyone driving or operating mobile plant and *pedestrians* means anyone on foot.

**C
14**

Accidents

The most common types of accident are listed below.

- ☑ Being struck by reversing or moving mobile plant.
- ☑ Loss of control, overturning when working, travelling across or manoeuvring on slopes.
- ☑ People falling when climbing in or out of the machine.
- ☑ Accidental operation of mobile plant that has been left with the engine running – often occurring as operators are getting in or out of the machine.
- ☑ Being crushed between a structure and mobile plant as it moves or slews around.

Many accidents involving mobile plant happen because plant is large and the operator has a restricted view. Extra mirrors and CCTV are sometimes fitted to improve the operator's all-round vision. You should not rely on CCTV and mirrors because, for example, a camera lens can be blocked by dirt which would affect the operator's ability to see you.

If you are close to moving or operating mobile plant you could be at risk. Whenever possible, stay within the designated pedestrian routes.

A mobile crane slewing, an excavator digging or a lorry tipping material, whilst not travelling, can still be a danger if you get too close.

Never assume an operator will see you in time to avoid you.

The movement of plant should be directed in situations where people could be at risk, such as when a lorry is reversing or when a crane is carrying out a lift.

 A vehicle marshaller controls the movement of plant. A signaller controls the movement of a crane or load being lifted.

If you are the operator and you lose sight of the person directing you, you must stop and locate them before continuing.

 Do not try to operate any item of plant if you are not trained, competent and authorised.

The chance of an accident between mobile plant and people on foot increases after dark. Even when wearing high-visibility clothing, if the lighting is poor the operator may still not see that you are there. The use of working lights should improve safety, but it is not a guarantee.

C 14

 After dark and at other times when light is poor, you will be harder to see.

Operator's field of vision is restricted

People have been seriously injured or killed when trying to pass too close to moving or reversing mobile plant.

Slewing plant

Clearance must take into account the reduced space if the crane tips

As the rear of a slewing crane or excavator turns, the gap between the rear of the machine and a fixed object (such as a wall, stack of materials or other plant) becomes much smaller (becoming a crush zone).

☑ If the gap is 600 mm or less during slewing then the gap should be fenced or blocked off.

If you are operating plant (such as a pedestrian roller or mobile elevating work platform (MEWP)), always be aware of what is behind or above – you may create your own crush zone.

This type of accident can and has happened because people on foot did not stay clear of mobile plant, took a short cut or followed a route that was not safe.

 Stay out of the crush zone. The shortest route may not be the safest route.

Management of mobile plant

Whether you are an operator or not, the site rules on the safe operation and segregation of mobile plant should be explained to you during your site induction.

A well-managed site will be organised to reduce the chance of accidents between mobile plant and people on foot. Measures, such as the following examples, will be in place.

☑ Separate site entrances for mobile plant and pedestrians.

☑ Separate routes for mobile plant and people on foot with barriers between them.

☑ One-way systems and site speed limits.

☑ Amber flashing beacons on mobile plant.

☑ All lights are working and switched on, where natural light levels are low and after dark.

☑ All visual aids (such as mirrors and CCTV) are clean and in good condition.

☑ Turning areas, so that reversing is banned or minimised.

☑ A vehicle marshaller to control movement of mobile plant.

Working safely

C 14

☑ Always wear your high-visibility clothing and keep it clean.

☑ If you cannot avoid passing close to mobile plant, or if you need to speak to the operator, you will have to be patient and wait in a safe place until:

- the operator knows that you are there, the plant stops operating and you are signalled to go past
- it has moved away altogether
- it has finished the job and stopped moving or working and the operator signals you.

☑ Stay out of plant compounds and other parking areas unless you are authorised to be there. Be alert to plant starting up and moving off, and keep out of its way.

☑ Do not ask for or accept rides on plant that is not designed to carry passengers. Deaths have been caused by unauthorised passengers clinging onto an item of plant then losing their grip and falling under the wheels or tracks.

☑ Report any aspects of plant operations that you think are hazardous to your supervisor or employer. For example, where mobile plant:

- uses routes that are only intended for pedestrians
- ignores one-way systems
- travels or operates too fast and is a danger to other people
- is operating too close for comfort
- looks to be defective.

Sometimes there isn't time to tell your supervisor or employer about a problem. If it is safe to do so, warn the operator and maybe others in the area. Your employer will still need to know about the problem. They can then make sure that the same situation does not happen again.

C
14

15

Lifting operations and equipment

What your site and employer should do for you

1. Use only competent and authorised people to plan, supervise and carry out lifting operations.

2. Provide lift plans (safe systems of work) for all lifting operations and make sure that you are briefed and understand them.

3. Make sure that lifting equipment and accessories are suitable for the task, inspected, maintained and examined.

4. Make sure that lifting equipment and accessories are marked with safe working loads.

5. Provide you with information and training so you can carry out the lifting operation.

What you should do for your site and employer

1. Follow any lift plan issued. Stop work and tell your supervisor if you cannot.

2. Only start work if you understand your role in the lifting operation and you are fit to work.

3. Carry out pre-use checks on equipment and report any defects before starting work.

4. Do not start work until defected items have been properly repaired or replaced.

5. Only act as a slinger/signaller if you are trained, competent and authorised to do so.

6. Attend all briefings as instructed by your supervisor.

7. Do not enter any exclusion zones unless authorised to do so.

C 15

Introduction

Poorly planned lifting operations can often go wrong resulting in fatalities or injuries to those involved or those in the area of the lifting operation, or causing damage to the structural failure or overturning of the lifting equipment.

Your employer must ensure the following.

☑ The lifting operation is properly planned by a competent person (often referred to as the appointed person, whose role is to develop/approve the lifting plan).

☑ The lifting operation is supervised by a competent person.

☑ The lifting operation is carried out in a safe manner.

Lifting a generator using a lorry loader

Accidents involving cranes and other lifting equipment are often caused by one or more of the following.

☑ Using the wrong type of lifting equipment or equipment with the wrong lifting capacity.

☑ Using lifting equipment incorrectly (unsafe technique).

☑ Failing to follow the lift plan (system of work) whilst carrying out the tasks.

☑ Poor assessment of ground conditions, overhead obstructions or changing weather conditions, such as high winds.

C 15

☑ Lack of co-ordination of crane movements when more than one crane is operating, and their arcs of movement overlap.

☑ Lack of training of the crane operators and signallers.

☑ Incorrect slinging of the load.

☑ Lifting a load of an unknown and underestimated weight or unknown centre of gravity.

☑ Poor inspection and maintenance of the equipment or accessories.

Examples of lifting equipment and accessories

Lifting equipment is any work equipment (such as cranes (mobile and static), hoists, telehandlers and excavators) that is used for mechanically lifting or lowering any load, including people.

☑ Scaffold hoists and gin wheels.

☑ Passenger/goods hoists.

☑ Telehandlers.

☑ Excavators being used as a crane.

☑ Rough terrain forklifts.

☑ Crawler, mobile and tower cranes.

☑ Mobile elevating work platforms (MEWPs).

☑ Lorry loaders.

There should be a lift plan for any operation being carried out by any form of lifting equipment. The depth of the plan will reflect the complexity of the operation. Work involving people at height or loads which are difficult to sling would be more complicated to plan and would require a more in depth and detailed lifting plan.

Inertia braked gin wheels are now common practice and far safer than traditional gin wheels

Lifting accessories are items of equipment used for attaching the load to the lifting equipment.

☑ Chains.

☑ Ropes

☑ Slings.

☑ Hooks.

☑ Shackles.

☑ Spreader-beams.

☑ Eye bolts.

Planning a lifting operation

All lifting operations **must** be properly planned by a competent person who will decide on how best to conduct a safe lifting operation. This information will be recorded in a lift plan (safe system of work).

The lift plan will need to consider the following (this list is not exhaustive).

☑ Weight of load to be lifted.

☑ The ground conditions and surrounding environment (such as waterways and highways).

☑ Overhead hazards (for example, a power line).

☑ Weight of the load to be lifted.

☑ Height of the lift required.

☑ Type of lifting equipment to be used.

☑ Selection of lifting accessories (for example, chains and shackles).

☑ Lifting team (for example, crane operators and slinger/signallers).

☑ Level of supervision required.

☑ Means of communication (for example, hand signals or two-way radios).

The lift plan will give information on any exclusion zones that are required to ensure the safety of people on site. You must not enter these zones unless authorised by the lift supervisor.

If you are involved in any lifting operation you must be briefed on the contents of the lift plan before work starts.

Inspections

A competent person must inspect all lifting equipment and accessories at suitable intervals – before first and every use, weekly and monthly. The frequency and type of inspection will depend on the potential for the item to fail. The inspections should include visual and functional checks.

Thorough examination

A periodic thorough examination must be carried out by a competent person. This will normally be a qualified engineer and is a very in-depth inspection that generates a report on completion. The report should be kept on file at the same location as the equipment or accessory.

Lifting equipment must be thoroughly examined as outlined below.

☑ When it is first used (unless bought brand new).

☑ If it is installed, after installation but before first use.

☑ If it is assembled, after assembly but before first use.

☑ At intervals not exceeding 12 months.

 Lifting equipment, used for lifting people, and all lifting accessories must be thoroughly examined every six months.

A MEWP should be thoroughly examined at least every six months

Hand signals for signallers

The following images are industry recognised hand signals for people directing the movement of lifting equipment.

Start

Stop

Raise

Lower

Left

Right

 You must not signal plant operators unless you are trained and authorised to do so.

Horizontal distance

Vertical distance

Move backwards

Move forwards

C
15

Danger

End

 The signaller should stand in a safe position, where they can see the load and can be seen clearly by the lifting equipment operator. They should face the operator if possible. Each signal should be distinct and clear. These signals have been reproduced from Schedule 1 of Health and Safety (Signs and Signals) Regulations.

(This contains public sector information licensed under the Open Government Licence v2.0.)

C
15

16

Working at height

What your site and employer should do for you

1. Avoid the need to work at height if possible.

2. Provide the correct work at height equipment and make sure it is inspected and maintained.

3. Provide a collective system to prevent falls (such as a scaffold, mobile elevating work platform (MEWP) or mobile tower).

4. Minimise any risk to you if there is a chance you could fall (such as by providing a harness, safety net or safe landing platform).

5. Give you information, instruction and training so you can work at height safely.

6. Make sure that all work at height is carried out in accordance with a safe system of work and that you are briefed fully.

What you should do for your site and employer

1. Follow the agreed safe system of work, and ask questions if you do not understand.

2. Use only equipment and methods you have been trained in.

3. Make sure you carry out pre-use checks on your equipment.

4. Not misuse any equipment.

5. Not take risks or short cuts.

6. Stop and seek advice if anything changes or seems unsafe.

D
16

Introduction

☑ Approximately half of all fatalities on construction sites are as a result of a fall from height.

☑ An average of seven people die each year as a result of falling through fragile roofs.

☑ Over half of all reported 'specified' injuries are due to either falls from height or a slip, trip or fall on the same level.

☑ Selecting the wrong type of work equipment results in many falls from height every year.

Many construction workers have sustained a life changing injury as a result of a fall from height. Such an event impacts not only the worker, but their family, lifestyle and ability to earn an income. It is vitally important that all work at height activities are adequately planned, assessed and the correct equipment selected and used to reduce the risk of injury.

 What can you fall from?

Many falls are from poorly secured ladders, faulty or poorly used stepladders or makeshift working platforms, which offer little or no fall protection.

About seven workers a year die after falling through fragile roofs. Others suffer serious injuries and disabilities as a result of falling.

For all work at height, measures must be taken to prevent the risk of any fall that could cause injury.

Work at height is work at **any** height where a person could fall and be injured. It also includes instances (such as working next to an open excavation) because of the risk of falling in.

D
16

What your employer should do

☑ Identify work that involves working at height.

☑ Plan the work to make sure that proper precautions and controls are in place.

☑ Select the right equipment for the work to be done.

☑ Make sure that people working at height have the right blend of training, knowledge, skills and experience, and that the work is adequately resourced and supervised.

☑ Tell the workforce the risks involved and the risk control measures to be followed.

☑ Make sure the equipment is regularly inspected and maintained and that defective equipment is taken out of service.

Planning the work

☑ A risk assessment must be completed for all work at height.

☑ The following should be taken into account.
  - The complexity of the work being done.
  - Who is doing the work and for how long.
  - Weather conditions and surface conditions (such as a wet, sloping roof).
  - How to raise and store materials and equipment.

☑ The emergency arrangements needed.

Hierarchy for working at height

Any person planning work at height should always follow a hierarchy of control and consider options at the top of the hierarchy before moving down.

Step 1. Avoid working at height
e.g. assemble on the ground and lift into position using a crane or by fixing guard-rails to structural steelwork on the ground before lifting and fixing at height.

↓

Step 2. Prevent falls from occurring
Use an existing safe place of work
e.g. parapet walls, defined access points, a flat roof with existing edge protection

↓

Step 3. Prevent falls through providing *collective* protection
e.g. scaffolding, edge protection, handrails, podium steps, mobile towers, MEWPs

↓

Step 4. Prevent falls through providing *personal* protection
e.g. using a work restraint (travel restriction) system that prevents a worker getting into a fall position

↓

Step 5. Minimise the distance and/or consequences of a fall using *collective* protection
e.g. safety netting, airbags or soft-landing systems

↓

Step 6. Minimise the distance and/or consequences of a fall using *personal* protection (The last resort)
e.g. industrial rope access (working on a building façade) or a fall-arrest system using a suitable, high anchor point

Requirements for working at height

☑ Safe access (such as a tower staircase or secured ladder) must be provided.

☑ Edge protection (such as temporary guard-rails) must be put in place.

☑ Remember that surfaces can become slippery in wet or frosty conditions.

☑ If you are working on or near to a leading edge then measures (such as a physical barrier or safety net) should be installed. A harness and fall-arrest lanyard must only be used as a **last resort**.

☒ You should **not** work on any structure where there is no protection from falls.

Fragile roofs

There are many fatal and serious injuries from people falling through fragile roofs and roof lights.

The following surfaces are likely to be fragile.

☑ Roof lights.

☑ Old liner panels on built-up sheeted roofs.

☑ Asbestos and fibre cement sheets.

☑ Metal sheets.

☑ Glass, including wired glass.

☑ Chipboard.

☑ Slates and tiles.

Asbestos and fibre cement sheets are obvious, but fragile roof lights, which look like the more secure surrounding roof structure over time, are not so obvious.

Many people are not aware that parts of a roof are fragile.

 You should not assume that a roof will support your weight or try to walk near the underlying supports.

D 16

All fragile roofs should be considered to be unsafe unless additional protection has been provided. It is sometimes difficult to see a fragile surface, especially if a roof is dirty, weathered, covered by moss or has been painted. Buildings with a fragile material roof covering should ideally show warning signage (as shown in the image below) but this will not always be the case.

Fragile roof and crawling board signs

A safe system of work **must** be put in place, and as a priority, work on a roof (particularly a fragile roof), should be avoided where possible. An example of an alternative safe system of work would be to work from underneath using a MEWP as a safe place of work to carry out the work at height. A safe system of work should also consider the following.

☑ Suitable access is provided (such as a stair tower or ladder) or using a MEWP.

☑ If the work has to be carried out from above the affected area, specialist working platforms with handrails should be provided. These are designed to span the roof purlins and evenly distribute the loading applied.

☑ Physical barriers or covers around or on fragile surfaces (such as roof lights or sky lights).

☑ The installation of safety netting, crash decks or airbags underneath the roof.

☑ Anchor points, fall arrest lanyards and safety harnesses.

☑ Arrangements for emergency situations, including how rescue will be carried out for casualties who have fallen into a safety net or are suspended by a harness.

 Never try to access or cross a fragile roof without a safe system of work.

Voids and holes

All holes and voids (such as those listed below) where a person could fall any distance and injure themselves must be protected.

☑ Floor and roof openings.

☑ Gaps in between floor joists and roof trusses.

☑ Lift shaft openings.

☑ Service holes and risers.

☑ Open manholes and other voids.

☑ Openings created during demolition.

☑ Open excavations.

☑ Openings created during site surveys.

All openings must be protected with secure barriers, covers, gates or doors, which are secured in position and display the relevant warning signs.

☑ Never remove a protective cover unless authorised to do so and you are protected against falling whilst the cover is not in place.

☑ If a hole, gap or void needs covering, you should report this to your supervisor straight away.

D
16

Properly constructed void protection, complete with appropriate signage

Scaffolding edge protection constructed around a void, complete with a scaffold tagging system

Preventing falls

If work at height cannot be avoided the best way to prevent people falling is by using physical barriers and equipment.

☑ Use scaffolding, mobile access towers, MEWPs, podium steps or other proprietary edge protection systems.

☑ The minimum height of the top guard-rail is 950 mm above the working platform.

☑ Gaps between guard rails and toe boards or the working platform must not be greater than 470 mm.

☑ Plastic barriers, netting or rope and pins are not suitable as edge protection as they are not rigid enough to prevent people from falling, unless they have been specifically designed for that purpose.

Correctly set up working platform with ladder access

Arresting falls

Fall-arrest systems include safety harnesses, soft-landing systems, safety netting and crash decks.

☑ If falls cannot be prevented then the risk of injury must be minimised.

☑ Arresting falls by means of harnesses and fall-arrest lanyards must be considered a last resort and is only acceptable when other methods (further up the work at height hierarchy of controls) have been considered and ruled out.

☑ The safe system of work must contain a procedure for emergency rescue.

D
16

Harnesses

Fall arrest harnesses are a type of PPE, and should only be used if falls cannot be prevented by physical barriers or minimised by using collective arrest systems (soft-landing systems, such as nets or air beds).

☑ Harnesses can be used to prevent a fall from occurring (fall restraint) and to minimise the consequences of a fall (fall arrest). Fall restraint is preferred to fall arrest (it is better to prevent the fall than arrest it).

☑ Choosing the type of harness and lanyard to be used is vital. Your employer should take into account where it is being used, how far the wearer may fall, any obstructions they may hit and any pendulum effect, (swinging from side to side after the fall has been arrested).

☑ You must receive formal training before using a harness and lanyard.

☑ It is vital you know how to inspect a harness for damage, how to fit it properly, where to attach it and **where not to attach it**.

 Never use a harness to work at height unless you have been trained.

A harness and lanyard could be all that prevents you from falling to your death. Make sure you clip on to a suitable anchorage point at all times.

There must be an effective rescue plan in place in case a person wearing a harness falls.

☑ They will need to be rescued quickly.

☑ When someone's fall is arrested and they are suspended in a harness they can experience a condition known as suspension syncope (where the person suspended faints and could suffer further complications).

Types of access equipment

D 16

Mobile elevating work platforms

☑ Common types of mobile elevating work platforms (MEWP) are scissor lifts and boom type (cherry pickers).

☑ You must only use a MEWP if you have been fully trained and are competent.

☑ If you are in a boom type MEWP you must wear a full body harness and restraint lanyard clipped to the designated attachment point in the basket.

☑ If the machine is fitted with additional ground level controls they should only be used in an emergency (for example, if the operator becomes incapacitated or unwell).

☒ **Never** clip onto a nearby structure.

☒ **Never** stand on the guard-rails of the MEWP, or lean out, especially when ascending or descending.

☒ **Never** climb out of a MEWP in an elevated position unless the unit has been specifically designed for that purpose.

Scaffolding

☑ Scaffolding must only be erected, altered or dismantled by trained and competent scaffolders.

☑ All working platforms must have double guard-rails and toe-boards fitted.

Good example of a warning incorporated into a physical barrier – do not access scaffolding if you see this sign

☑ Keep the scaffold working platform clean and tidy. These areas should not be used for storage unless specifically designed and designated for this purpose.

☑ You should always follow the safe loading information.

☑ Brick guards must be fitted if materials are stored above toe-board height or if there is a risk of tools or materials falling and striking someone below.

☒ You must never interfere with scaffolds or remove any components, no matter how simple it appears to be.

☒ You must never overload scaffolds.

Mobile access towers

Mobile access towers are a safe and versatile form of access equipment if used correctly. Unfortunately, many access towers are not erected or used correctly, and, as a result, become unstable and are the cause of many accidents.

You should hold a Prefabricated Access Suppliers' and Manufacturers' Association (PASMA) or equivalent qualification to erect, alter or dismantle a mobile access tower.

The training should cover how to reduce common risks associated with this type of equipment and include information on the following.

Safe working on a mobile tower, with toe-boards and guard-rails in position and wheels locked

☑ Manufacturer's instructions for safe use.

☑ Positioning of the equipment – it is positioned on level ground.

☑ It is not being used so close to an overhead power line that a person could make direct or indirect contact with the power line.

☑ Use of locking wheel brakes.

☑ Fitting of advanced guard-rails at a lower level to provide edge protection at the level above, without putting the operative at risk during installation.

☑ Checking that guard-rails and toe-boards are fitted (these must not be removed).

☑ Assessing loading capability (how much weight can be placed on any platform).

D 16

123

You must make sure of the following.

☑ Towers are not overloaded.

☑ Only the internal ladder is used to access the decks.

☑ Working platforms are not fitted too high, so that guard-rails are too low.

☑ Prevent/prohibit over-reaching.

 If you are only working on a mobile access tower and not involved in erecting, altering, dismantling or moving it, you should receive a toolbox talk on the risks and hazards associated with your work as a minimum. A toolbox talk will not give you the knowledge, skills, experience or authority to erect, adapt, dismantle or move the tower.

Podium steps

Podium steps have become a popular piece of access equipment and can provide a safe and efficient means of achieving low-level access if used correctly.

☑ They are a safe and versatile form of access equipment, providing a safe working platform if used correctly.

☑ They allow you to work from the working platform facing every side without it becoming unstable.

☑ Some podium steps are fitted with power to allow you to adjust the height easily. Some are fitted with anti-surfing features which prevent you from pulling yourself along when you are on the equipment.

☒ They can be unstable and topple over if not built or used correctly.

Podium steps in use, correctly assembled and wheels locked

 You must always use the brakes when using the podium steps. Do not pull yourself along when you are inside it.

Stepladders

There are many types of stepladder on the market. Some offer good fall protection and others less so.

Stepladders should only be considered as suitable in the following circumstances.

☑ Where a risk assessment has shown the use of other more suitable equipment is **not** reasonably practicable.

☑ The work does not involve pulling or pushing motions.

☑ The work does not require applying pressure.

☑ The work is of a short duration, 30 minutes or less.

Wherever possible, platform steps should be the preferred option over traditional swing-back steps.

Stepladder with integrated side guard-rails for additional protection

☑ Always check they are in good condition before use.

☑ Always use on firm, level ground.

☑ Always make sure they are fully extended and face forward towards the steps.

☑ The stepladder and you should always face the work (you should not need to twist your body to face the work, as doing so would side load the steps).

☑ Three points of contact should be maintained where possible.

☑ Report any defects to your supervisor.

☒ Never over reach or apply a side loading.

☒ Never stand on the top three treads of any stepladder unless it is designed to be used that way.

D
16

Ladders

☑ Working from ladders should be considered as a last resort.

☑ They should only be considered for light work of short duration (less than 30 minutes is recommended), for work that does not involve pulling or pushing motions or the application of pressure, and where the use of other work equipment is not appropriate.

☑ They are most often misused when used as a working platform.

☑ A risk assessment must have validated the use of a ladder to demonstrate that it is not reasonably practicable to use other means or methods.

☑ It is essential that those who use ladders are trained and competent to do so.

☑ Always check they are in good condition before use.

☑ A painted ladder can hide defects or damaged parts.

☑ Report any defects to your supervisor.

☒ Ladders should not be used near overhead power lines.

If ladders are used, they **must** meet the following criteria.

Ladder at 75° (one out to four up)

☑ Be of the correct type – Class 1 industrial or BS EN 131 light trades.

☑ Be in good condition.

☑ Be placed on firm and level ground.

☑ Not be at risk of being struck by vehicles.

☑ Use outriggers if available.

☑ Be set at the correct length and angle for the job – **75°** or a ratio of **1:4 (one out to four up)**.

☑ Be properly secured (tied at the top).

☑ If being used as a means of access, extend one metre past the stepping off point.

You should have three points of contact at all times.

Ladders are classified into the following three different grades.

☑ Class 1 industrial.

☑ BS EN 131 light trades.

☑ Class 3 domestic (for domestic use only, and should **never** be used in a construction environment).

Class 1 industrial ladders are recommended for use in construction environments as they offer the highest duty rating.

**D
16**

17

Excavations and confined spaces

Excavations and confined spaces

What your site and employer should do for you

1. Assess the project and identify where working in a confined space or excavation may be necessary, and inform you.

2. Assess the risks and develop a safe system of work.

3. Make sure that anyone entering a confined space is properly trained and adequately resourced.

4. There are adequate resources to prevent collapse, and a safe system of work is in place where it is necessary to enter an excavation.

5. Make sure that there are provisions and procedures in place to prevent people, materials and vehicles from falling into excavations.

What you should do for your site and employer

1. Do not enter a confined space or excavation unless a safe system of work is in place and you are trained, competent and authorised to do so.

2. Do not enter any excavation which is unsupported.

3. Install supports following the safe system of work.

4. Do not take any risks.

5. Do not leave any confined space or excavation open or unguarded.

D
17

128

Introduction to excavations

An excavation is any hole or trench dug into the ground as part of construction or utility work. Some excavations are knee deep, but many are deeper. They do not need to be deep before becoming a serious risk or a confined space.

Every year deaths and injuries occur due to excavations collapsing, workers being overcome by poisonous gases or striking live services.

Excavations and trenches **collapse** for the following reasons.

☑ The sides are not supported or supports are not installed properly.

☑ Vehicles operate too close to the edge (for example dumpers, excavators and/or other large vehicles).

☑ Materials and spoil are stored too close to the edge.

☑ The ground dries out, shrinks and collapses.

☑ Heavy rain weakens the ground and the sides.

☑ The excavation undermines or weakens nearby walls and structures, causing them to collapse.

 Excavations are dangerous

A cubic metre of soil can weigh **over a tonne** (1,000 kg).

A shallow excavation can easily collapse onto you.

It can crush your legs, hips or chest and prevent you breathing.

Collapse is silent and without warning.

D
17

Safe working in a deep excavation using trench boxes and a tied ladder

Examples of good practice are listed below.

☑ Avoid the need for anyone to go into an excavation.

☑ Install excavation supports before anyone goes into an excavation.

☑ Use methods that protect the person installing the support system.

☑ Prevent vehicles from coming too close, (for example, using wheel stop blocks).

☑ Provide a safe way to get in and out (such as a tied ladder).

☑ Only work within the safety of the protected area on long open excavations, (for example, within the confines of a drag box or trench supports).

☑ Provide fall prevention around the excavation, (for example a handrail or extended trench sheets).

A competent person must inspect the excavation before the start of each shift or after any event (such as heavy rainfall) that may have affected the strength or stability. Something may have happened to affect the excavation's stability or something may have fallen from or into it. All inspections must be recorded, and defects corrected immediately.

Keep vehicles a safe distance away from the edge of an excavation. A truck carrying 6m³ of concrete weighs approximately 26 tonnes.

Poisonous or flammable gases and fumes

Poisonous gases and fumes (such as those listed below) can be heavier than air and can 'pour' over the edges and start filling up an excavation or a confined space.

- [✓] Exhaust fumes from petrol or diesel-powered plant.
- [✓] Naturally occurring gases (such as methane) which seep out of the ground.
- [✓] Fumes or vapours from solvents (such as welding plastic pipes, epoxy resins or sealants).
- [✓] Liquefied petroleum gas (LPG). Carbon dioxide (CO_2) and other pipe freezing gases.

Safe systems of work may include the following.

- [✓] Using a gas detector to test the air before entry and then monitoring continuously.
- [✓] Pumping in fresh air.
- [✓] Using a solvent-free product that does not give off fumes.
- [✓] Wearing breathing apparatus as a **last resort**.

Always be aware of gas hazards

You may not be able to see or smell gas in an excavation or a confined space.

If you are in an excavation or a confined space and feel light headed, dizzy or can smell gas: **warn others – get out – stay out – report it immediately.**

Underground services

Underground services include the following.

- [✓] Electricity cables.
- [✓] Gas mains.
- [✓] Water mains.
- [✓] Sewers and drains.
- [✓] Telecommunications or fibre optics.
- [✓] Oil or fuel pipes.

Thousands of service strikes happen every year. Many result in serious injury and some are fatal. It is vital that any excavation work, no matter how big, small, deep or shallow, is properly planned.

Before any excavation or digging, every effort should be made to locate existing services. These methods will show roughly where the services are.

☑ Refer to service drawings.

☑ Contact the utility company.

☑ Carry out a ground radar survey.

☑ Use cable avoidance tool detection (such as CAT and genny equipment).

Hand digging trial holes to expose the services is the most accurate way of locating them.

Examples of the services you are most likely to find and their relevant colours are shown below (this list is not exhaustive).

Service	Colour
Electricity (all voltages)	Black or red
Water	Blue, black or grey
Gas	Yellow
Communications	Grey, white, green, purple or black

The table above describes utility industry practice. However, it should not be assumed that all apparatus will conform to the recommendations for colour coding.

Underground services

Safe systems of work may include the following.

☑ Not using forks or other bladed tools near live underground services.

☑ Always treating services as live until confirmed otherwise.

☑ Never assuming a service runs in a straight line.

☑ Not using power tools or excavators within 500 mm of the indicated line of a service.

If you find an unexpected underground service, report it immediately.

D
17

If you strike a live service – if it is safe to do so, move away, do not go back, warn others and report it.

Introduction to confined spaces

Workers can become trapped or overcome by fumes, vapours, poisonous or explosive gases when working in confined spaces. This can lead to people dying.

 Many workers who tried to rescue workmates without a proper rescue plan and the necessary equipment have been overcome by toxic or suffocating gas and fumes, or a lack of oxygen and have collapsed and died, adding to the tragedy.

What is a confined space?

Confined spaces are not just tanks, vessels or chambers. They do not have to be totally enclosed.

They can be any place where there is a risk of the following.

☑ Reduced or increased levels of oxygen in the air.

☑ The presence or build up of poisonous gases, fumes or vapours.

☑ The presence or build up of flammable or explosive gases or vapours.

☑ Drowning due to an inrush of liquid, or being engulfed or buried in free flowing solids (such as sand).

Depending upon the work hazards many places could be classed as a confined space. Some examples are listed below.

☑ Excavations and trenches.

☑ Manholes, inspection chambers, sewers and soakaways.

☑ Service tunnels and shafts, plant rooms and boiler rooms.

☑ Basements, voids and staircases.

☑ Lofts, roof voids and attic spaces.

☑ Unventilated rooms and rooms with sealed windows.

☑ Oil storage tanks or water tanks above or below ground.

An unventilated room may not seem like a confined space. However, if you are using a substance in the room that gives off toxic or hazardous vapours then you could be overcome and fall unconscious.

D
17

Hazards

Reduced oxygen levels

Oxygen, which we need to breathe, can be reduced in the following ways.

☑ By hot works or machinery that burns up the oxygen.

☑ Through people breathing.

☑ By rust inside enclosed tanks.

Build up of poisonous or flammable gases

Oxygen can be replaced by asphyxiating, toxic or flammable gases by the following.

☑ Stirring up sludge or slurry in excavations may release methane or hydrogen sulphide.

☑ Natural methane venting from the ground or rotting vegetation.

☑ Using substances that give off fumes or vapours (such as solvents, paints and resins).

☑ Sewage giving off hydrogen sulphide (which smells like rotten eggs and will drive out/dilute the oxygen in the air).

☑ Chalky ground, which gives off carbon dioxide, especially when wetted by acidic rain.

☑ People breathing out carbon dioxide.

☑ Gases (such as LPG, methane or oxygen enrichment) which build up to form a highly flammable atmosphere.

An overturned tanker or a large spill may release petrol or dangerous chemicals into the drainage system. The vapours can travel hundreds of metres.

**D
17**

Working in a confined space

Your employer should identify if the work activity, hazards and area of work is or should be classed as a confined space. Anyone working in a confined space must be properly trained.

Work in a confined space needs safety documentation to produce a safe system of work.

☑ A suitable and sufficient task and site specific risk assessment.

☑ Method statement, including a rescue plan.

☑ Permit to work (to manage entry and control).

Excavations and confined spaces

Emergency exit from a confined space using escape breathing apparatus (EBA)

The safe system of work will identify important issues, such as those listed below.

☑ Safe access and egress, how to get in and out safely.

☑ What tools and materials to use, and how they should be used.

☑ The type of air and gas monitoring equipment and alarm system.

☑ Who can enter and for how long (time limits).

☑ What personal protective equipment (PPE) and respiratory protective equipment (RPE) to use.

☑ The emergency arrangements.

☑ The rescue equipment and trained rescue team.

The air within the space must be tested before entry, and constantly monitored while the space is occupied using a meter with an audible and visual alarm. If the alarm sounds, the area must be evacuated as quickly and safely as possible. There should be one person (called the 'top man' or 'attendant') at the entrance to the confined space whose job is to raise the alarm and start the rescue plan if things go wrong.

 Never try to rescue someone unless you are part of a properly trained and equipped rescue team. Use the time to get expert help and call the emergency services.

D
17

134

18

Environmental awareness and waste control

What your site and employer should do for you

1. Develop procedures for avoiding pollution and tell everyone involved.

2. Provide means to distribute, store and use materials to avoid damage.

3. Provide means to dispose of waste correctly.

4. Explain any specific environmental issues at site induction.

5. Provide emergency response methods (such as spill kits).

What you should do for your site and employer

1. Turn off plant, equipment and taps when not in use.

2. Reuse materials where possible.

3. Avoid creating too much dust or noise.

4. Dispose of waste correctly.

5. Know where the spill kit is, how to use it and report any incidents.

E
18

Introduction

The construction industry is the single biggest consumer of resources in the UK, using around 420 million tonnes of materials each year. The industry also generates a huge amount of waste (around 120 million tonnes each year); about 20 million tonnes of waste goes to landfill, including 10 million tonnes of new, unused building products.

The poor management of materials and resources on a construction project can lead to excessive amounts of waste. This is costly, bad for the environment and it can be unsafe.

The following are some ways that waste can be generated.

☑ Poor design.

☑ Incorrect or over-ordering.

☑ Incorrect storage and management of materials leading to damage.

☑ Poor workmanship.

Sustainability

You will increasingly hear the word sustainability being used in connection with construction work. The drive to carry out construction in a sustainable way affects everyone in and around the industry.

One element of sustainability is to carry out construction work in a responsible way and to minimise any environmental damage, which could otherwise cause problems for future generations.

Collecting rainwater for reuse

Examples of good practice are listed below.

☑ Designing out waste such as making the unit off site, making site dimensions to match standard product sizes, or adjusting site levels to reduce the amount of excavated material going off site.

☑ Looking after the people who carry out construction work, and using local labour and services to support the local economy.

☑ Using locally produced materials and minimising transportation of raw materials and finished goods.

☑ Saving energy and water wherever possible by turning off equipment when not in use.

☑ Not damaging the environment by causing pollution.

☑ Using reclaimed materials or materials with a high recycled content.

☑ Using timber and other wood products that can be fully traced to sustainable managed forests.

E
18

☑ Reusing left over materials wherever possible to conserve raw materials and save the energy it would take to produce new.

☑ Segregating waste into different types so that it may be reused or recycled more easily.

 Fuel, energy, water, construction materials and time are often wasted on construction sites, practices which need to be stopped or at least reduced.

Environmental responsibilities

Responsibilities of the person in charge of the site

The person in change of the site has contractual and legal responsibilities to make sure of the following.

☑ The client's environmental requirements are implemented and met.

☑ Environmental planning conditions are implemented.

☑ Environmental damage is prevented during construction.

☑ Harmful substances, including fuels, are stored and handled correctly to prevent spillage or pollution.

☑ Employees are trained how to use spillage response equipment (for example, spill kits).

☑ Materials are properly segregated into different types of waste.

☑ Only registered waste carriers are used.

☑ Waste is properly disposed of through licensed contractors and facilities.

☑ Accurate records and documentation are kept for all wastes.

They should also work out ways of preventing, reusing or recycling as much waste material as is practical in line with the waste management hierarchy and industry commitments to reduce waste to landfill.

E 18

Your part in preventing environmental damage

You should be given instructions and advice during and after site induction so you understand the following.

☑ The site's environmental rules (such as how to dispose of your waste).

☑ What damage your work can have on the surrounding environment.

☑ What work controls will be applied to avoid damage.

☑ What you need to do as an individual.

☑ What to do in an emergency (for example, how to use a spill kit properly).

Pollution

Causes of pollution

☑ Deliberately or accidentally allowing substances (such as cement, silt, grout, sewage, chemicals, oils/greases or vehicle fuels) to soak into the ground or contaminate rivers, streams and ditches.

☑ Deliberately or accidentally allowing waste to escape from the site, contaminating adjacent land and/or watercourses.

☑ Not segregating contaminated materials from other waste (for example putting rags used to clean up an oil spillage in with general waste materials).

☑ Allowing smoke, fumes or dust to contaminate the air.

☑ Causing too much noise, light or vibration, which can affect the quality of life of people who live or work nearby.

☑ Allowing noise, dust or other polluting substances to disturb or destroy the habitats of protected or invasive plants and species of wildlife.

Why pollution occurs

☑ Substances enter rivers, streams, ditches, drains or the ground because they aren't stored correctly.

☑ Not having properly protected storage areas, to contain the leaks or spills of harmful liquids, (for example, oils, fuels and solvents).

☑ Allowing the build-up of hazardous substances or waste materials, resulting in them being washed into the ground by rainwater.

☑ Failing to adequately protect waste material skips, resulting in rainwater washing harmful residues out.

☑ Rain and muddy surface water running off site onto roads, into drains and watercourses.

☑ Not having the equipment, or a plan to control accidental spillages.

☑ The poor maintenance of plant and equipment allowing fuel and other leaks, and excessive noise or air pollution.

☑ The illegal burning of waste materials and fly tipping.

A spill involving just one litre of oil can contaminate one million litres of drinking water.

E
18

Your part in preventing pollution

To avoid creating pollution you should always adhere to the following.

Spill kit deployed

☑ Follow the instructions in the control of substances hazardous to health (COSHH) assessment and any site rules when using any substance, particularly with regard to storage and disposal.

☑ Keep the lids on tins of paints, adhesives and solvents when not in use.

☑ Keep oils, fuels and chemicals within bunded areas when not in use.

☑ Prevent spillages, particularly into open ground, by careful handling and decanting of harmful liquids.

☑ Minimise the waste of materials by storing anything that can be rain-damaged under cover.

☑ Keep harmful substances at least 10 m away from watercourses, drains, and so on.

 Pollution spreads easily

Spilt or leaking oils, including fuel, can be particularly damaging to the environment.

It is possible for spilt or leaking substances to soak deep into the ground and pollute groundwater, which in some cases becomes domestic drinking water.

5 litres of oil can contaminate an area **the size of two football pitches.**

If it gets into the **groundwater,** pollution may appear **several miles away.**

 Spilt materials must be properly contained using absorbent materials, not washed down with detergent.

When refuelling site vehicles or construction plant, this must be carried out in an area with a hard surface that prevents spilt fuel from soaking into the ground. The following points should be implemented if refuelling has to be carried out away from these areas, where the ground is unprotected.

☑ A drip tray must be used (this must be cleared of any spilt fuel afterwards by using absorbent spill clean-up materials).

☑ Refuelling must take place at least 10 m from watercourses or drains. (Where 10 m cannot be achieved speak with your supervisor who should then put in place further control measures.)

 Regulatory bodies recommend that refuelling is always carried out under supervision.

**E
18**

Where possible, refuelling should be carried out using a pumped supply through a nozzle fitted with an automatic cut-off to prevent over-filling and therefore spillages. Where necessary, funnels should be used to assist in preventing spills

Do not dispose of harmful substances into drains or gullies. Site drain covers should be colour coded to show what is allowed to pass through the drain.

Blue	Surface water (such as clean, uncontaminated rainwater).
Red	Foul water (such as sewage and silty run-off water).
Red 'C'	Combined surface and foul water.

If the product you are using displays this sign on the label or COSHH assessment then it is harmful to the environment. Anything left over, including the container, must be disposed of in line with the label and site rules.

Ground that was used or built on before may contain hazardous substances. You must immediately **stop** and tell your supervisor if you find either of the following.

☑ Soil that has a strange smell and/or appears to be oily.

☑ Fragments or clumps of fibres that could be asbestos or other hazardous materials.

If you are involved in pumping water out of an excavation (de-watering) you must be aware that silty water must be treated before it can be discharged into surface water drains or ditches. Site management or your supervisor must make the decision upon whether the water is silty.

Pollution incidents

If you are aware that an environmental incident or spill has occurred then act quickly and follow these simple steps: stop – contain – notify.

☑ **Stop** work, assess the situation, raise the alarm and notify your supervisor. Make sure that you have appropriate PPE and wait for help if needed. **Do not put yourself at risk.**

☑ **Stop, contain and take action** to prevent further contamination, by righting oil drums or closing a leaking valve for example. Stop the contamination from spreading by using spill kits or building earth or sand bunds, directing flows away from unprotected drains.

☑ **Eliminate** all sources of ignition. Do not allow plant to be switched on or off.

☑ **Notify** your supervisor or employer of an incident as soon as possible.

☑ **Cover** drains or manholes to stop the substance entering unprotected drainage systems.

☑ **Check** the spill has not reached any nearby drains, manholes, watercourses, ditches, ponds or other sensitive areas.

☑ **Dispose** of all contaminated materials (such as absorbent granules, soil or cleaning cloths) used to contain the spill in the correct hazardous waste skip.

E
18

Report the facts to your supervisor or employer, who should notify the Environment Agency (in England) or Natural Resources Wales (in Wales), by the emergency hotline: 0800 80 70 60.

Waste materials

Environmental damage can result from waste materials in the following circumstances.

☑ If it is allowed to accumulate and is not protected from the weather and scavenging animals.

☑ Where hazardous waste is mixed with other waste (such as asbestos cement mixed with rubble).

☑ If it is illegally disposed of or fly tipped.

Everyone has a part to play in preventing environmental damage by being aware of the potential environmental risks that arise from their work.

Your employer has a responsibility to identify how and where they create waste so that efforts can be made to cut the amount produced. Always check if someone else can use what you are about to throw away as it might have a use elsewhere.

Segregated waste bins

Different types of waste should be segregated into different skips so that they can be recycled more easily. Recycling waste means that it does not have to go to landfill.

To assist, colour coded labels are often put on skips to show what type of waste should be put in them. *(Refer to the table on the following page.)*

Label colour	Waste
Bluc	Metallic
Green	Wood and timber
White	Gypsum and plaster
Orange	Hazardous
Brown	Packaging
Grey	Inert
Black	Mixed non-hazardous
Red	Asbestos
Yellow	Clinical/biological

 Hazardous waste must never be mixed in with other types of waste.

If hazardous waste gets into landfill it can be damaging to the environment.

Examples of hazardous waste

☑ Asbestos.

☑ Batteries.

☑ Used spill kits.

☑ Fluorescent light tubes.

☑ Waste solvents (such as white spirit, oil and bitumen based paints).

☑ Epoxy resins and mastics.

Oily rags segregated into hazardous waste containers

E
18

Nuisance

No-one on site, or off it, should have to suffer nuisance and possibly ill health because of site activities.

Talk to your supervisor if you think that the work you are doing might be causing a nuisance to other people. This may be the case if you are carrying out any of the work activities listed below.

Managing dust and emissions

☑ Creating delays and congestion on local roads because of poor traffic management planning and logistics.

☑ Causing noise, particularly during unsocial hours.

☑ Creating vibration that can be felt off site.

☑ Mud or dirt being deposited on public roads or footpaths.

☑ Vehicle fumes causing a nuisance to nearby properties or people.

☑ Generating smoke and dust.

☑ Creating off-site dust clouds from haul roads.

☑ Site lighting or task lighting shining onto nearby properties or people, including road traffic.

E
18

19

Demolition

What your site and employer should do for you

1. Provide you with a written demolition plan (including a sequence of events, the relevant risk assessments and method statements) identifying the correct sequence of demolition and methods to prevent premature or accidental collapse.

2. Provide you with suitable and sufficient information, instruction, training, resources and supervision.

3. Provide suitable and sufficient risk assessments and method statements indicating the safety procedures and other procedures to be followed.

4. Provide suitable and sufficient welfare facilities, plant and equipment.

5. At no time place you in danger or expect you to take unnecessary risks or expose you to uncontrolled hazards or risks.

6. Give you training so that you are competent and can work safely and in safety.

What you should do for your site and employer

1. Follow the agreed safe system of work, comply with the requirements of risk assessments and method statements, working safely at all times. Stop work and notify your supervisor if you are unable to do so.

2. Not take risks with your own or anyone else's health or safety.

3. Report anything that you feel is unsafe or a threat to health.

4. Keep to any permit systems, site rules and procedures that are in operation and do not operate plant unless you are trained and authorised to do so.

5. Attending briefings, training and health surveillance as requested.

6. Look after and wear the personal protective equipment (PPE) and respiratory protective equipment (RPE) required for the job.

Introduction

Demolition is a highly specialised and potentially dangerous activity. Health and safety law requires that it is carried out by trained and competent demolition contractors.

Demolition work can be of any size or scope, it is not always on a large scale. Demolition work is any demolition, dismantling or structural alteration of any size, such as the removal of a single wall in a domestic house.

☑ Before starting any demolition project, the risk assessment must be reviewed to identify the intended way of controlling the hazards.

☑ A competent person must be appointed to supervise the work before it starts.

Planning the work

The demolition contractor must make sure that the work is planned and carried out in such a way that it avoids danger or, where this is not possible, reduces the danger as far as is reasonably practicable. This will include the following requirements.

☑ Identifying the location of any asbestos through a refurbishment or demolition survey carried out before work starts, by a trained and competent asbestos surveyor.

☑ Identifying, locating and isolating all services.

☑ Identifying hazardous materials or substances and planning their removal.

☑ Recording the arrangements for health and safety in writing before the work starts, (construction phase plan).

☑ Setting out the sequence of operations in a written demolition plan and ensuring that it is read out during site induction and understood by all involved.

☑ All persons involved in planning, managing and carrying out demolition work must be competent, (have the right blend of skills, knowledge, training and experience, together with the correct level of supervision).

Safe methods of working

Given the potentially hazardous nature of demolition work, it is essential that safe methods of work are developed and followed.

☑ Make sure that the site is secure to prevent unauthorised access, particularly by children outside working hours.

☑ Make sure that there is enough clear signage, (for example, indicating the boundary of exclusion zones).

☑ Make sure all known and unrequired services are isolated, disconnected and made dead. If underground services that were not identified earlier are discovered, work must stop until a safe method of work has been agreed.

☑ The electricity company or the cable owner must be consulted if work has to be carried out near to overhead cables.

F
19

☑ Work at height must be avoided where possible. Where such work must be carried out, it should be carefully planned and carried out to prevent the fall of people or materials.

☑ If demolishing internal brick walls, you must work across in even courses, from the ceiling down.

☑ A gas-free certificate must be obtained before carrying out the demolition cutting of any fuel, slop or waste tank.

☑ Gas-free certificates are normally only valid for a single eight hour shift after being issued.

☑ Do not allow combustible waste materials (demolition soft strip materials arising from the works) to accumulate.

Health hazards

Due to the nature of the working environment demolition can present some potentially serious, long-term threats to the health of the people involved if the risks are not controlled. Health issues are often overlooked because of the long-term nature of some diseases and the fact that workers move around between different projects.

☑ Lead-based paint might be present under asbestos clad or coated steelwork.

☑ Where asbestos is suspected of being or is potentially present a demolition survey must be carried carried out prior to the work commencing so that the asbestos may be safely removed or otherwise (encapsulated and) protected. before any demolition work begins.

☑ If, during demolition, it is suspected that some asbestos-containing material or other hazardous substance (for example old lead painted steelwork) remains in the structure, work must stop immediately and a supervisor must be told.

☑ Control of Substances Hazardous to Health (COSHH) assessments must cover any other harmful substances likely to be released.

☑ Demolition is likely to release airborne dust (such as silica). (The need for respiratory protective equipment (RPE) is covered later in this section.)

☑ Skin diseases (for example, dermatitis), must be prevented by making sure that there is no skin contact with harmful substances.

☑ If you have been involved in the hot cutting of coated steel you must be aware of the potential for exposure to harmful levels of lead in the blood.

☑ If you have come into contact with lead you must wash your hands and face before eating, drinking or smoking.

☑ Exposure to vibration in your hands and arms can lead to vibration white finger.

☑ The safe system of work must prevent exposure to hand-arm vibration which can be caused by using equipment, (for example, breakers or drills).

F
19

Examples of tools that could cause hand-arm vibration if control measures are not implemented

Personal protective equipment and respiratory protective equipment

Wearing the correct personal protective equipment (PPE) and respiratory protective equipment (RPE) can help prevent exposure to harmful substances. The wrong type of PPE or RPE is likely to be useless. A competent person must carry out a risk assessment to ensure that the correct grade and type of RPE is selected and worn. The assessment should be made following the guidance in HSG53 Respiratory Protective Equipment at Work a practical guide. Your supervisor must make sure that the correct PPE and RPE is being worn, as in the situations below, for example.

☑ Depending on the protection required, a minimum of FFP3 half mask with a suitable filter, for higher risks, a higher grade RPE may be required.

☑ If you are working in a toxic or low oxygen atmosphere, a compressed airline breathing apparatus or self-contained breathing apparatus is needed.

☑ An air-fed respirator or helmet will be needed if you are cutting coated steel work.

 Respirators are not suitable RPE for a low oxygen environment. Their value is limited in a toxic or dusty environment because of the effectiveness of the filter which can become saturated and blocked.

 Anyone using RPE must be face-fit tested and instructed on its maintenance and use.

F
19

Plant and equipment

Anyone who has to operate any item of plant or equipment (for example a mobile elevating work platform) must be trained, competent and authorised.

☑ Information on the daily checks for mobile plant can be found:
- in the manufacturer's handbook
- in information provided by the supplier of the machine
- on stickers attached to the machine.

☑ Full daily checks must be carried out by the operator as instructed in the manufacturer handbook and/or instruction manual that was supplied with the machine.

☑ All plant movements and traffic routes must be planned and coordinated to make sure of the following.
- There is safe access to and egress from the site.
- Pedestrians are safe.
- There is no conflict between different types of vehicles.
- The movement of materials is safe.

☑ An item of plant that is defective must be isolated so that no-one else can try to use it and its condition must be reported.

☑ Machines that operate in areas where there may be falling materials must be fitted with a falling object protective structure (FOPS).

☑ Roll-over protective structures (ROPS) must be fitted to plant to protect the driver where there is a danger of it rolling over.

☑ The head and tail lights and obstruction lamps of any machine must be switched on especially when the plant is operating in all conditions of poor visibility.

☑ Operators must never try to move a machine if they do not have adequate visibility from the driving position (such as losing sight of the vehicle marshaller).

☑ All plant must be inspected, with the details recorded, at least every week.

☑ Operators must face the machine when climbing down from it.

☑ Passengers must only be carried on construction plant if a purpose-made passenger seat and passenger restraint (seat belt) is fitted.

☑ Unattended mobile plant must be left in a safe place, with the keys removed and the doors locked.

F
19

Lifting operations

All lifting operations and use of equipment must be thoroughly planned especially when carrying out demolition works. There is an increased risk of falling (unsupported) materials. Poorly thought out lifting operations, and the use of defective equipment have been the cause of many accidents.

☑ A method statement (lifting plan) must be drawn up for all lifting operations.

☑ All lifting operations must be carried out within the safe working load (SWL) of any item of lifting equipment or lifting accessory used.

☑ The SWL must be marked upon each item of lifting equipment and each lifting accessory (such as chains, shackles, slings and strops).

☑ Lifting equipment used for lifting people, and all lifting accessories must be thoroughly examined every six months, all other lifting equipment should be thoroughly examined every 12 months.

☑ If an item of lifting equipment or lifting accessory is found to be defective it must not be used. The item must be isolated so that no-one can use it. This is known as placing an item in quarantine.

☑ Anyone not involved in the lifting operation should be kept out of the area.

Confined spaces

Working in confined spaces is well known as a potentially hazardous activity. Many people have died through lack of planning, training or access to the correct equipment. People have also died when trying to rescue others who have got into difficulty, often because of a lack of planning, training or suitable equipment.

No-one should be involved in confined space work unless they have been fully trained, are assessed as medically fit for the task, and are properly equipped and authorised.

☑ Before entering a confined space a suitable and sufficient risk assessment and safe system of work, and emergency rescue plan, must be drawn up. Everyone who is going to be involved in the operation must be fully briefed on, and understand, the safe system of work including emergency rescue procedures.

☑ During confined space working it is essential that the people doing the work strictly keep to and follow the safe system of work.

☑ Depending on the situation (the reason for the entry), the task to be done and the location of the confined space, the safe system of work may involve the issue of a permit to enter/work and or other permits.

F
19

Carbon dioxide extinguishers must never be taken into a confined space as they dilute the air of oxygen and pose a higher risk of asphyxiation.

LPG, other gases and substances

By the nature of demolition activities, and the type of work that will be carried out, it is more than likely that highly flammable and explosive substances will be stored and used on site at some time.

☑ LPG cylinders that are used for heating or cooking in a site cabin must be stored outside the cabin.

☑ It is essential that gases are stored a safe distance away from other gases, (for example oxygen cylinders must be stored more than 3 m away from LPG cylinders).

☑ The correct type of fire extinguishers must be available where petrol or diesel are being stored. Water extinguishers must **not** be provided.

☑ Flashback arrestors must be fitted between the pipes and gauges when using oxy-propane cutting equipment.

☑ Cans or drums of fluids must be stored in bunded areas to prevent any leaks from spreading.

☑ If unlabelled drums or containers are discovered, work must stop until they have been safely dealt with.

LPG store

20

Highway works

What your site and employer should do for you

1. Develop safe methods that offer you maximum protection from road users and hazards.

2. Train you if you work on any live highway.

3. Train you if you operate mobile plant or equipment.

4. Provide, maintain and inspect the correct plant and equipment.

5. Provide the correct personal protective equipment (PPE) for tasks and high-visibility clothing for the road type.

What you should do for your site and employer

1. Follow the step-by-step safe system of work and site or highway traffic rules.

2. Position signs and cones in the right sequence and in the correct place.

3. Do not work in the safety zone and do not use hand signals to control traffic.

4. Wear your task specific PPE (high-visibility clothing, seat belts, and so on) at all times.

5. Report any defects and complete any required daily and weekly inspections.

F
20

Signing, lighting and guarding

The working environment on the highway will involve you working with, or alongside, pedestrians and moving traffic and may lead to problems rising from confusion, conflict and delays.

To reduce this, a clear and concise **signing, lighting and guarding** procedure must be put in place.

Temporary traffic management (TTM) forms the basis of warning, informing and directing the pedestrian and the road user, through and round the site, by the means of signs, cones, and barriers. Most of the common situations are described in the Code of Practice *(Safety at Street Works and Road Works)* – the *Red book*. Further advice can be found in Chapter 8 of the *Traffic signs manual*.

Safe works – basic principles

- ☑ To comply with health and safety legislation, a safe system of work in respect to signing, lighting and guarding will need to be in place. The safe system of work must be based on a suitable and sufficient risk assessment.
- ☑ It is management's responsibility to provide equipment in good condition – it is your responsibility to use it in the correct way.
- ☑ It is your responsibility to sign, guard, light and maintain your works safely.
- ☑ You will need to wear high-visibility clothing whether visiting or working on the site.
- ☑ Drivers must be able to see the advance warning signs. Where visibility is poor, or there are obstructions, extra signs should be provided. Signs should be set out for traffic approaching from all possible directions.
- ☑ You may have to duplicate warning signs on both sides of the road (for example where signs on the left-hand side are hidden by heavy traffic).
- ☑ You must include the works area, working space and safety zone in the area to be marked off with cones (and lamps if necessary). Never use a safety zone as a work or storage area.
- ☑ If there are temporary footways in the carriageway, or obstructions (such as stored materials or plant, not already within the working space), sign and guard them separately to the same standard.
- ☑ Signs, lights and guarding equipment should be secured by bags of granular material placed at low level, to avoid them being moved by wind or passing traffic.
- ☑ Check regularly, at least once every day, that signs and cones have not been moved, or become damaged or dirty.
- ☑ In many cases traffic control will be necessary.
- ☑ Traffic conditions may change from those expected and alterations may be needed. If in doubt consult your supervisor.
- ☑ On finishing the work make sure that all plant, equipment and materials are removed quickly from the site. All signs, lighting and guarding equipment must be removed immediately when they are no longer needed – it is a legal requirement.

F
20

Works vehicles

All works vehicles should be of a conspicuous colour and must have an amber warning beacon. Any vehicle entering a site must switch on the amber beacon. This reduces the risk of having been followed into the site by private vehicles; should this occur you will need to assist the driver to leave the site via the nearest safe designated exit.

Site layout

The site layout consists of the following.

☑ Advance signing – length depends on the speed and type of road.

☑ Works area.

☑ Working space.

☑ Safety zone, including the following.

    – Lead-in taper.

    – Longways clearance.

    – Sideways clearance.

    – Exit taper.

Setting out signs

The safety zone is provided to protect you from the traffic and to protect the traffic from you. You may only enter it to maintain cones and other road signs. Materials and equipment must not be placed in it. The sideways clearance is the space between the working space and the moving traffic and varies with the speed limit. If pedestrians are diverted into the carriageway, you must provide a safety zone between the outer pedestrian barrier and the traffic. If the carriageway width does not permit the full sideways clearance you must consult your supervisor. It may be necessary to divert traffic or reduce speeds to below 10 mph.

 Don't work in the safety zone – you may lose more than your hat.

Setting out the site

You are at greatest risk when setting out the site, so you must make sure the following precautions are in place.

- ☑ Switch on your flashing beacon(s).

- ☑ Stop the vehicle in a safe place.

- ☑ Put on your high-visibility clothing.

- ☑ Get out of the vehicle on the passenger side where possible.

- ☑ Observe traffic movement at all times.

- ☑ Position signs in the correct sequence, at the correct distance and where they can be seen clearly – they must not cause a hazard to pedestrians.

- ☑ Secure the signs with sandbags (if necessary).

- ☑ Check that all of the signs are correct before starting work.

Traffic management and control systems

Pedestrian movement

Footway working may mean the re-routing of pedestrians. You may need to provide a temporary footway, of a minimum width as specified in the Code of Practice, using barriers (with tapping rails for the blind or visually impaired), ramps and information signs.

Footpath diversion showing the safe pedestrian route

Motorways and high speed dual carriageways (50 mph and above)

Extra precautions are necessary when working on motorways and high speed dual carriageways including the following.

- ☑ All traffic management must be undertaken by a registered traffic management contractor.

- ☑ Advance warning signs need to be duplicated on the central reservation.

- ☑ If you are entering a site on a motorway, you must switch on your flashing amber beacon and the correct indicator about 200 m before the access point, to give following traffic enough advance warning.

- ☑ Long sleeved high-visibility clothing must be worn.

F
20

Short stop/mobile working operations

These include continuous mobile operations (such as hedge trimming), as well as those which involve movement with periodic stops (for example gully emptying) and short duration works (for example pothole filling). This work must only be carried out where there is good visibility and during periods of low risk (such as light traffic flow).

The basic requirements for the works vehicle are listed below.

☑ It must be conspicuously coloured.

☑ It must have one or more roof-mounted amber flashing beacons operating.

☑ A keep right/left arrow sign must be displayed on or at the rear of the vehicle, showing drivers approaching on the same side of the carriageway which side to pass. This directional sign must be covered or removed when travelling to and from the site.

This is the minimum traffic management needed for short stop/mobile operations.

Advance warning signs are necessary when there is not enough space for two-way traffic to pass the works vehicle or where it cannot be seen clearly. The signs should be placed up to one mile from the works vehicle.

Under no circumstances should you use hand signals to control traffic. Only the police are legally allowed to do this.

The *Red book* describes the various systems, where and when they may be installed, and should be consulted in all cases.

Give and take

☑ Speed limit 30 mph or less.

☑ Coned off area 50 m or less.

☑ Drivers approaching the works can see at least 50 m beyond the end of the works.

☑ Traffic, including heavy goods vehicles, is light.

Priority signs

☑ Coned off area 80 m or less.

☑ Drivers approaching the works can see at least 60 m beyond the end of the coned area for 30 mph speed limit. Other distances are given for different speed limits.

☑ Two-way traffic flow is light.

Stop/go boards

☑ Works length can be up to 500 m depending on two-way traffic flow levels.

☑ Normally use stop/go boards at each end of the works.

☑ Where visibility is impeded, a communication system must be employed.

☑ Allow enough time for traffic to clear with both boards showing 'stop'.

☑ Consult your supervisor if the works are near a railway level crossing or a road junction.

Portable traffic signals (temporary traffic lights)

☑ Works length can normally be up to 300 m.

☑ Signals must be put up and removed in an organised way and specific sequence.

☑ Allow more time for slow-moving traffic, cyclists and horse riders, by increasing the all-red timings.

☑ Most sites will only need one set of signal heads. Where visibility is poor a double-headed system should be used.

☑ Where signal cables cross the carriageway, cable protectors must be used and the signs ramp/ramp ahead must be used.

☑ If the detector systems become faulty, you must operate the signals on fixed time or manually, and contact the service company or your supervisor.

Mobile plant

The movement of mobile-operated plant and vehicles causes many accidents and serious injuries on sites every year. The accidents involve not only the operator, but people close by or just walking past.

Mobile plant means all mobile plant and site vehicles that can move either under their own power or by being towed.

Operator means anyone driving or operating mobile plant.

Pedestrians means anyone on foot.

Maintaining mobile plant

If you are an operator you are responsible for daily and weekly maintenance to make sure your plant and/or equipment is in a safe condition, giving particular attention to the following.

Operative being trained on pre-use checks

☑ Checking levels of fuel, oil, water and brake fluid.

☑ Ensuring the horn, flashing beacon, lights and indicators all work.

☑ Making sure that brakes, including hand and parking brakes, are operating efficiently. Where air brakes are fitted the air storage tanks must be drained at the start of every shift.

☑ Making sure windscreen wipers and washers operate efficiently, including keeping the washer bottle topped up.

☑ Keeping windows and mirrors clean, and correctly adjusted for good visibility. This is particularly important when manoeuvring.

☑ Keeping the cab clean, tidy and clear of any loose articles that may obstruct the operation of foot pedals and controls.

☑ Checking that your clothing, especially if you are a wearing a jacket, does not snag on controls/dead man switches.

F
20

Diesel must never be used to clean mobile plant or prevent bitumen or asphalt sticking to buckets or load beds, as this will make it slippery and present a serious risk of injury from slips and falls. Use suitable access equipment to prevent serious injury from falls when hosing down plant, especially for high level or load beds of lorries and gritters. Carrying out this type of work is working at height, as there is a risk of injury if you fall.

 Mobile plant in an unsafe condition must not be used.

Operating mobile plant

If you operate plant you must be trained and competent to operate the type of plant you are authorised to use. You should have a suitable driving licence and/or plant operator's certificate/card. Before operating any plant for the first time, you should read and understand the manufacturer's operating instructions and be familiar with the controls and their function.

- ☑ You must not work too many hours (the Drivers' Hours Regulations and Working Time Regulations limit the number of hours that may be worked in any day or week).

- ☑ Operator and plant record books must be completed where necessary.

- ☑ You must be aware of the gross vehicle weight, the maximum axle weights and overall dimensions of the plant.

- ☑ When refuelling any plant, remember, no smoking or naked lights and switch off the ignition.

- ☑ You are responsible for the safe operation and condition of your mobile plant at all times.

- ☑ You must comply with road traffic legislation and site rules where applicable.

- ☑ The use of an amber beacon does not exempt you from compliance with the Highway Code.

- ☑ You must stop operations immediately and report defects that present a serious risk to the safe operation of plant (for example, faulty controls).

- ☑ Where fitted, seat belts must be worn (they could save your life).

- ☑ When manoeuvring, use mirrors and CCTV, if fitted.

- ☑ A vehicle marshaller must be used when reversing in areas where there may be pedestrians.

- ☑ Do not operate mobile plant too close to any excavation, no matter how shallow. Stop blocks are the preferred method of preventing mobile plant getting too near to an excavation when tipping.

- ☑ Obey all speed limits, height restrictions, direction and warning signage.

- ☑ Be alert to the dangers of colliding with or clipping scaffolding, temporary works, mobile towers, mobile elevating work platforms (MEWP) and ladders.

F 20

Parking

- ☑ Where possible, park on level ground in a designated area, clear of pedestrians. Handbrake/parking brake should be on, engine off and key removed.

☑ If you cannot park on level ground you may need to chock the wheels or otherwise prevent unIntended movement of the plant.

☑ All hydraulic equipment (such as buckets, forks and back-actors) should be lowered to the rest position.

Access

☑ Only authorised people should be allowed onto mobile plant.

☑ Passengers may only be carried on mobile plant equipped with sufficient, suitable seating for them.

☑ Wait until the mobile plant has come to a complete stop before getting on and off. Never jump down – always use the steps and grab rails.

☑ Maintain three points of contact with access ladders or hand/foot holds.

☑ Never, at any time, work under an unpropped mobile plant body.

 Maintain three points of contact – don't jump down.

The following operations may need detailed consideration and risk assessment to work out safe access.

☑ Maintenance.

☑ Working at height at the top of the mobile plant, including the sheeting of loads.

☑ Anywhere else where falls may be likely.

Loads

Loading and the load are the operator's responsibility.

☑ Plant must not be overloaded and loads must be spread evenly and secured.

☑ Operators of mobile plant should not remain in the seat or cab while it is being mechanically loaded.

☑ Drivers must check sideboards, curtains, sheeting and tailboards are fastened and secure before moving off.

☑ Drivers must check load for security. Any projections must be properly marked and clearly visible.

☑ Care should be taken when removing lashings as the load may have shifted during transit or moved when being released.

☑ Loading and unloading of tippers must be attended by a competent vehicle marshaller. Rear end tippers are liable to overturn whilst tipping on uneven or unmade ground.

☑ People should stay well clear of any tipping or loading operations.

☑ Tippers and dumpers must not travel with the bucket in the raised position after the load has been discharged.

F
20

Trailers

Before towing any trailer or plant, you must make sure you have the correct class of driving licence. It is essential that the driver is licensed for the specific combination (towing vehicle plus trailer and load).

☑ The towing vehicle and trailing vehicle must be compatible and any conversions properly secured with the correct towing pin. Home made and lashed up connections are not acceptable.

☑ When being towed on a highway the trailer must be fitted with registration number plates, indicators, brake and rear tail lights.

☑ Where fitted, trailer parking brakes must be applied before disconnecting the trailer from the towing vehicle. On slopes, trailer wheels should also be chocked.

☑ Trailers fitted with independent operating brakes should be connected to the towing vehicle by a cable, which will activate the trailer's brakes if the tow hitch fails. Otherwise the trailer must be fitted with a safety chain connected to the vehicle.

 Loads should not be secured to sheeting (rope hooks) as they have no safe working load. Loads must only be secured to designated load securing points and rings, using appropriate chains and strops.

Mobile plant used for lifting

☑ All lifting operations should be properly planned by a competent person.

☑ Only authorised and trained operators should operate lifting equipment.

☑ All lifting equipment and lifting accessories should be subject to a daily and pre-use visual inspection.

All lifting operations should be properly planned

☑ Care must be taken when operating extending booms or other lifting equipment near to overhead power lines. The safest method is limiting the boom extension or height of the mast, so it does not go in to the overhead exclusion zone.

☑ Equipment for lifting people (such as a MEWP) must be thoroughly examined every six months.

☑ Other lifting equipment must be thoroughly examined every 12 months.

 The rated safe working load (SWL) of any lifting equipment must never be exceeded.

F
20

21

Specialist work at height

What your site and employer should do for you

1. Make sure work at height is properly planned so that your place of work at height and the access route to and from it are safe to occupy.

2. Provide, inspect and maintain the most suitable work at height equipment.

3. Provide adequate safety equipment to prevent falls, or if necessary to arrest any falls.

4. Give you a written safe system of work which you fully understand so that you can work at height safely.

5. Make sure you are trained and regularly updated in methods of working safely at height.

What you should do for your site and employer

1. Fully understand and follow the agreed safe system of work (including using any equipment provided to prevent or arrest falls).

2. Do not use powered access (or any other) equipment unless you have been trained and authorised.

3. Not interfere with anything provided for safety.

4. Not take risks or short cuts.

5. Report any falls which occur, even if they cause no injury.

6. Report any unsafe aspect of your work or work conditions that you feel may be unsafe.

Introduction

☑ Every year many deaths and serious injuries result from falls from height.

☑ All too often the same types of accidents reoccur (such as falls through fragile roof materials and falls from ladders).

☑ In many cases taking basic safety precautions and/or providing training could have prevented suffering.

 You should also read Chapter D16 Working at height, which explains what employers and in some cases you must do to comply with the law and keep yourself, and others, safe whilst working at height.

Safe working at height

Safely working at height depends upon the following.

☑ The work being properly planned with a safe system of work in place, which follows the hierarchy of control for working at height.

☑ The people who will carry out the job being adequately trained, competent and authorised.

☑ The job being carried out in line with the safe system of work.

☑ Adequate supervision being provided.

☑ The tools and equipment to be used are properly maintained and inspected.

Before you start working at height (for example on a roof) there are many things that your employer, or you, should do to make sure that the job is carried out safely. Some examples are shown below.

☑ Assessing the risks arising from the work and taking measures which will:

  – prevent people or materials falling from height

  – make sure that there are no serious injuries or damage if someone or something does fall.

☑ Drawing up a method statement that explains exactly how the job should be carried out and making sure that the people doing the job understand it. The method statement should include details of the following.

  – How falls will be prevented.

  – The equipment to be used.

  – Who will supervise the job.

  – The sequence of operations that must be carried out.

If you are not sure that what you have been asked to do is safe or you are unhappy about any other aspect of working at height, you should talk about it with your supervisor.

F
21

Specialist work at height

Generally, the risks will depend on the following.

Working at height in a safe environment

☑ The nature of the place of work (for example a scaffold platform or leading edge of a new roof).

☑ The method of access chosen to get the people doing the job to the place of work.

☑ Details of the safety precautions and rescue plan in case someone does fall.

☑ The number of people who will be working at height.

☑ The length of time that people will be working at height.

☑ How experienced the people are in doing the job they need to do.

☑ The nature of any materials that will have to be hoisted and/or stored at height.

☑ The method of hoisting materials.

☑ The weather.

☑ Whether or not people can be kept out of the area below where the work is taking place.

 Falls are still the biggest killer, but many could easily have been prevented.

Hierarchy for working at height

Any person planning work at height should always follow a hierarchy of control and consider options at the top of the hierarchy before moving down.

Step 1. Avoid working at height
e.g. assemble on the ground and lift into position using a crane or by fixing guard-rails to structural steelwork on the ground before lifting and fixing at height.

Step 2. Prevent falls from occurring
Use an existing safe place of work
e.g. parapet walls, defined access points, a flat roof with existing edge protection

Step 3. Prevent falls through providing *collective* protection
e.g. scaffolding, edge protection, handrails, podium steps, mobile towers, MEWPs

Step 4. Prevent falls through providing *personal* protection
e.g. using a work restraint (travel restriction) system that prevents a worker getting into a fall position

Step 5. Minimise the distance and/or consequences of a fall using *collective* protection
e.g. safety netting, airbags or soft-landing systems

Step 6. Minimise the distance and/or consequences of a fall using *personal* protection (The last resort)
e.g. industrial rope access (working on a building façade) or a fall-arrest system using a suitable, high anchor point

F
21

Roof work

Much work that is carried out at height involves working on roofs, which can be hazardous.

☑ Roof work is particularly dangerous because it is not always clear at the start whether or not the roof cladding is a fragile material. A safe system of work must be in place for all work at height.

☑ Fragile roof lights can be dangerous if not barriered-off or covered with securely fixed covers that can withstand any load imposed on them.

☑ Remember that surfaces can become slippery after rain, frost, snow and where moss is present.

☑ High-level features (such as overhead cables) present further danger.

☑ If you are working near power cables check with your supervisor or the person in charge of the site that it is safe to be on the roof.

☑ Specialist access equipment is likely to be needed for carrying out work above fragile roofs (for example the inspection of pipework).

☑ Materials must be stored on roofs in a safe way so that:
  - they do not pose a hazard to anyone working on the roof
  - the pitch of the roof is taken into account when deciding what can be stored safely
  - a safe method of getting them up to the roof is employed (for example inclined hoist, scaffold-hoist, safety pulley or gin-wheel)
  - during loading-up excessive 'point loading' is avoided
  - they cannot fall, or be blown off, the roof
  - they can be accessed safely
  - they can be safely and quickly distributed around the roof to where they are needed.

If you are planning to use a roof ladder consider the following.

Typical roof ladder in use

☑ Whether a roof scaffold is a better option.

☑ A stable working platform at eaves height will provide safe access to the roof ladder with the added feature of edge protection.

☑ If a roof ladder is to be used, it must be purpose made or a normal ladder fitted with a proprietary fitting.

☑ If using a leaning ladder for access, the transition between the two ladders must be safe.

☑ A leaning ladder used for access must be stable and extend 1 m above eaves height.

Means of access

Scaffolds

A common way of preventing falls is to use a secure and stable working platform (such as a scaffold). Below are some essential considerations when using scaffolds.

☑ Is it a safe and suitable means of access for the job that has to be done (for example are the lift heights satisfactory)?

☑ They must only be erected, altered and dismantled by a person who is trained and competent. The scaffolder should hold a current industry recognised CISRS card.

☑ Edge protection must be fitted to all working platforms.

☑ Each working platform must be wide enough to allow the job to be carried out safely, and for the passage of people and equipment as necessary.

☑ Every scaffold must be inspected periodically by a competent person, with the findings of the inspection entered in a register. Details may also be recorded on a plastic tag, usually fixed to the scaffold next to the access point.

☒ Never overload working platforms; this has been the cause of many scaffold collapses.

☒ Untrained, unauthorised people should **never** interfere with a scaffold in any way (for example by removing a tie or guard-rail which is in their way).

Typical scaffold tagging system

 If you notice any unauthorised modifications to a scaffold, report it to your supervisor straight away.

F
21

169

Mobile elevating work platform

Common types of mobile elevating work platform (MEWP) are cherry pickers (boom type) and scissor lifts. Safety considerations when using a MEWP are shown below.

☑ You must not operate any type of MEWP unless you are trained, competent and authorised. Holding an IPAF card is a good indication of training, but is not an authority.

☑ Users of cherry pickers must normally wear a safety harness and restraint (fixed-length) lanyard secured to the designated anchorage point. Unless a documented risk assessment dictates otherwise.

☑ The MEWP chosen for the task must allow safe access to the place of work. If it does not reach, a larger machine is necessary. Do not stand on the guard-rails or put a stepladder or hop up on the working platform.

☑ Operators must know how to carry out daily and weekly checks.

☑ The person planning the task must make sure that a survey is carried out to identify any overhead hazards or underground voids (such as drains or cellars) which could collapse under the load.

☑ Only use a MEWP in areas covered by your lift plan, as ground conditions may not have been assessed in other areas.

☑ Before elevating the machine, operators must identify any projections or other features on the structure which could trap them between the guard-rails and the structure.

☑ Wind speed forecasts should be obtained before work commences.

☑ The Beaufort Scale gives managers and workers indicators of prevailing wind conditions. The scale categorises the wind strength between Force 0 and Force 9. The higher the number the higher the wind speed (for example Force 2 is a light breeze and Force 7 is a near gale).

☑ Operators must be aware of the wind-loading on a raised MEWP and be prepared to stop work and lower the machine if the wind speed is judged to be too high.

☑ There must be a rescue plan in place in case the operator is stuck or injured and cannot lower the working platform.

☑ The ground-level controls must only be used in an emergency (for example if the operator becomes ill or is trapped).

☑ A MEWP must not be used as a substitute for the stairs in the structure being worked on.

Ref. IPAF D1

Emergency descent symbol

Note: *if there is an emergency, a responsible person on the ground should know where to find and use the lowering controls (sometimes shown by an emergency descent symbol).*

Never carry more than the maximum safe load in a MEWP. The maximum load in kilogrammes or number of people will be shown in your lift plan and displayed on the machine.

Mobile access towers

☑ Mobile access towers can be static or mobile, depending if wheels are fitted.

☑ They can be built from tube and fitting scaffold components or more commonly prefabricated alloy frames which slot together.

Tube and fitting towers must only be erected, altered or dismantled by a trained and competent scaffolder (for example someone who holds a CISRS card).

Alloy towers must only be built, altered or dismantled, in line with the manufacturer's instructions, by someone who has been trained and is competent on that type of tower (for example someone who holds a PASMA card).

Listed below are some safety considerations.

☑ The ground or floor surface must be level and sufficiently firm to take the loading of the base plates (static) or wheels (mobile).

☑ The guard-rails and toe-boards must be fitted before the tower is used.

☑ Some types of alloy towers have guard-rails that can be positioned before the working platform is accessed.

☑ The brakes must be on at all times when a mobile tower is in use.

☑ Once the platform of a mobile tower has been occupied the trapdoor must be closed immediately to prevent anyone or anything falling through it.

☑ Provision must be made for the safe hoisting of tools and materials up onto the platform.

☑ Every tower must be inspected periodically by a trained, competent and authorised person, including an inspection after any event that is likely to have made it unsafe to use (such as impact by a vehicle or being subjected to severe wind or weather).

☒ The working platform must only be accessed by using the built-in ladder (**never** climb up the outside of a tower or use a free-standing ladder).

☒ A mobile tower must not be moved whilst any person(s) or equipment are on the platform.

Ladders and stepladders

More stable items of access equipment are often now available for tasks that, at one time, would have been carried out using a ladder or stepladder. Ladders and stepladders should only be used for access to places of work at height and for carrying out light work of short duration where the risk of a fall is low. A properly carried out risk assessment will show whether a ladder or stepladder is a suitable item of access equipment to use for any particular job. The risk assessment **must** also show that there was no more suitable means of access or working platform for a particular task or workplace, other than to use a ladder or stepladder.

F 21

If the risk assessment shows that a ladder or stepladder is the most appropriate equipment, the consideration must be given to the following areas.

☑ Any ladder used on construction sites must have been manufactured for industrial use and will be labelled 'Class 1, Class 2, or BS EN 131' (light trade). Any ladder labelled 'Class 3' is for domestic use only and is not suitable for use on a construction site.

Some considerations for ladder inspections

☑ Apart from the class of ladder, possible defects, including splits in the material (from which the equipment is manufactured), missing or distorted rungs or frayed, broken or missing tie-cords.

☑ Make sure that where a ladder is used for access to a high-level platform or similar, there is a landing at least every 9 m (about 30 foot) that the ladder rises vertically.

☑ Make sure that an access ladder extends at least 1 m above the stepping-off point if there is not another handhold.

☑ Various fittings (such as those below) are available that allow ladders to be used safely.
   – Stand-off frames that avoid the need to rest ladders against fragile or flexible materials (such as plastic guttering).
   – Anti-slip mats and other anti-slip devices upon which the styles are positioned.
   – Adjustable stabilisers to prevent sideways slipping.
   – Adjustable extensions to allow use on sloping ground.
   – Ridge-hooks that allow an ordinary ladder to be converted to a roof ladder.

☑ Ladders are made from various materials.
   – Generally alloy ladders are lighter than wooden ones but will conduct electricity and so cannot be used close to live overhead cables.
   – Fibreglass ladders are non-conducting and so are safer to use near electrical supplies or electrical equipment.

 All types of ladder will conduct electricity if they are wet.

☑ If you are planning to use an extending ladder consider the following.
   – Keep the minimum overlap between sections, as given in the manufacturer's instructions.
   – The latching mechanism (and hoisting rope/fittings if appropriate) must be part of the pre-use inspection.
   – The length/weight of the ladder and how many people will be raising it will decide whether it is safer to extend the ladder before raising it.
   – Look for overhead obstructions **before** raising the ladder.

F
21

Preventing falling objects

One of the obvious dangers of working at height is the possibility of materials, equipment, hand tools, and so on being dropped or thrown onto anyone below the place of work. Working at Height Regulations prohibit the throwing or deliberate dropping of any item of plant, equipment, material or substance from a place of work at height. Measures that should be taken to prevent this are listed below.

☑ Being aware of the presence of people, including passers by, below the work area.

☑ Fitting edge protection to the working platforms of scaffolds.

☑ Storing materials awaiting use in a safe way, away from the edges of flat roofs.

☑ Consider fitting a short lanyard with a wrist-loop to hand tools.

☑ Wearing a chin-strap with a safety helmet to prevent it falling off if you need to bend over while working.

☑ Rigging a safety net, overlaid with a fine mesh.

☑ Using a waste chute, with the bottom just above a skip, to move waste materials to a lower level. Consideration should be given to shrouding or covering the skip to limit the creation of dust and dust clouds as a result of using the waste chute.

Fall arrest (protecting you if you do fall)

Health and safety law recognises that there will be situations where physical barriers cannot be used, and the use of collective fall arrest measures (such as safety nets or airbags) is not practical. In these circumstances individual fall arrest measures (such as harness and lanyards) may be used as a **last resort**.

The following items should be considered when your employer chooses fall arrest measures.

☑ Collective fall-arrest systems, (such as safety nets or airbags), are preferable to personal protective measures (such as a harness and lanyard).

☑ A safety harness and lanyard should only be used in situations where:

– it is not practical to use other fall arrest measures (such as a safety net or airbags)

– a purpose-designed, secure anchor point is available (integral or mobile anchor)

– users have been trained in the pre-use inspection, fitting and use of the equipment

– users are aware that any damaged equipment must not be used

– the workplace must be designed or secured, and the work must be planned to avoid a pendulum effect in case someone should fall

– a rescue plan is in place to reduce to a minimum the time that someone is suspended in a harness. An injured person's condition can deteriorate rapidly if they do not receive medical attention quickly. A person not injured in a fall may suffer injury from a prolonged suspension (suspension syncope, where the suspended person faints and suffers from further complications).

F
21

☑ Essential features of any harness used for fall arrest are shown below.

- A full body harness will keep someone who has fallen in an upright position until rescued.
- Ideally it will be fitted with a feature that allows the person to raise their thighs above horizontal or to 'stand up' whilst awaiting rescue, releasing the pressure caused by the leg straps and reducing the chances of further injury.
- It must be inspected before use, with more detailed periodic inspections at intervals set by the employer.

Safety nets

☑ Safety nets should be rigged immediately below where people are working to minimise the distance a person could fall.

☑ Safety nets must be rigged by someone trained, competent and authorised to do so.

☑ Nets must be periodically inspected and any damaged nets replaced.

☑ If any damage to a safety net is discovered, work above the net must stop, the damage must be reported, and the net replaced or repaired by a competent person.

☑ Materials or debris that have fallen into the net must be quickly cleared from it.

☑ Alterations and repairs to safety nets must only be carried out by a trained, competent and authorised person.

☑ No-one other than a trained and competent net rigger should interfere with the securing cords. If you find one is in your way, report the problem.

☑ Nets are often rigged using a MEWP, the floor surface must be suitable and able to withstand the loading.

☑ If a MEWP cannot be used it may be necessary to employ competent rope-access technicians to rig the nets, (for example Industrial Rope Access Trade Association (IRATA) trained technicians).

Safety nets installed prior to roof works commencing

Airbags/bean bags

These systems can be an effective method of arresting falls, if they are installed correctly. They are generically known as *soft-landing systems*.

☑ They must be supplied and installed by competent contractors.

☑ They must be clipped together as necessary to provide a continuous fall protection area.

☑ They must fill the area over which fall arrest protection is needed.

☑ Airbags must not be too big; if over-size they will exert a sideways pressure on anything that is confining them and they may not inflate as designed.

F
21

☑ Airbag inflation pumps must be kept running whenever anyone is working above them.

☑ Care must be taken to make sure that anyone who falls cannot bounce or slide onto another hazard (for example onto exposed rebar or out of a first floor window).

Rope access

☑ Rope access is a specialised activity requiring particular skills and training.

☑ Anyone engaged to carry out rope access must be IRATA or similar industry trained.

☑ Generally, rope access is needed where it is impractical to provide a working platform, other fall prevention methods or fall arrest measures.

☑ Tasks that rope access can be used for include the following.

  – Structural surveys.

  – Non-destructive testing.

  – Localised concrete repairs.

  – Cladding/glazing panel replacement.

  – Secondary fixings.

  – Surface preparation and decorating.

  – Pressure pointing.

Rope access system
(Image supplied by PETZL)

F
21

F
21

22

Lifts and escalators

What your site and employer should do for you

1. Make sure that a competent person plans and supervises the work.

2. Provide you with a method of working that is safe and without risks to your health.

3. Explain the safe way of working to you, which will be in a method statement and risk assessment.

4. Provide you with adequate information, instruction and training.

5. Provide you with the right tools and equipment for the job.

What you should do for your site and employer

1. Follow the agreed safe system of work.

2. Use only equipment and methods you have been trained in.

3. Wear the right personal protective equipment (PPE) for the task.

4. Do not take risks or short cuts.

5. Stop and seek advice if anything changes or seems unsafe.

Overview and control measures

By the nature of the equipment, work on lifts and escalators can be hazardous and must only be taken on by trained, competent and authorised staff.

The Lift and Escalator Industry Association (LEIA), which is responsible for the lift and escalator specialist section, represents most of the lift and escalator companies in the UK. Its members are committed to the LEIA safety charter, which requires member companies to work in line with BS 7255 and BS 7801.

The actual requirements for this training and competence are detailed in Code of Practices BS 7255 *Safe working on lifts* and BS 7801 *Safe working on escalators and moving walks*.

Members should make sure, in particular, that all of their employees undertake the following.

- ☑ Use and verify **stop** and other devices when accessing, egressing and working on car tops and in lift and escalator pits to ensure total control of the equipment.

- ☑ Electrically isolate and lock off, when power is not needed and when working close to unguarded machinery.

- ☑ Protect themselves and others from falls and falling objects.

These are just three essential control measures that must be implemented to make a safe working procedure.

For further guidance refer to:

Lift and Escalator Industry Association
33–34 Devonshire Street
London
W1G 6PY

Tel: 020 7935 3013
Fax: 020 7935 3321

www.leia.co.uk

F
22

F
22

23

Tunnelling

What your site and employer should do for you

1. Make sure that a competent person plans and supervises the work.

2. Provide you with a method of working that is safe and without risks to your health.

3. Explain the safe way of working to you, which will include a risk assessment and method statement.

4. Provide you with adequate information, instruction and training.

5. Provide you with the right tools and equipment for the job.

What you should do for your site and employer

1. Follow the agreed safe system of work.

2. Use only equipment and methods you have been trained in.

3. Wear the right personal protective equipment (PPE) for the task.

4. Do not take risks or short cuts.

5. Stop and seek advice if anything changes or seems unsafe.

Introduction

Due to the nature of tunnelling, where people are often working far underground and a long way from a place of safety in the open air, the importance of working in a way which is safe and free of risks to health cannot be stressed enough.

The following text highlights some of the common potential hazards that could be experienced during tunnelling operations. The risk control measures and safe systems of work identified follow BS 6164, which is the Code of Practice for health and safety in tunnelling in the construction industry.

Safe systems of work

Formal safe systems of work are essential during tunnelling operations. Some examples are listed below.

☑ Making sure that where a shaft is being constructed, provision is made for:

- adequate guarding
- continuous gas monitoring
- ventilation.

☑ Understanding that falling objects or failure of the load is the greatest danger from suspended loads during shaft sinking operations.

☑ Wearing a safety harness when building rings from a platform within a shaft.

☑ Making sure of continuous structural stability by immediately installing supports to excavated ground.

☑ During tunnel construction, use compressed air (where and when necessary) to prevent or reduce the ingress of water.

A training tunnel
(© Crossrail Ltd)

☑ Storing tunnel segments in a secure way that prevents:

- falling or collapse
- any other movement
- instability.

☑ Making sure that personal protective equipment (PPE), safety signs and notices, and a rescue plan are provided.

☑ Using water-spray curtains to help reduce the movement of smoke through a tunnel.

☑ Protecting against the rebound or fall of materials during and after sprayed concrete operations.

☑ Taking great care to make sure that oxygen cylinders do not come into contact with grease, to avoid potential explosions.

F
23

☑ Make sure there is a safe system of work for track maintenance workers and locomotive drivers, including the provision of the following.
- Flashing lights either side of the work area.
- Adequate refuge points.
- A permit to work.
- A lookout person.
- Everyone involved in the job wearing high-visibility clothing.

Communication

Effective communication is essential for safe tunnelling operations. For this reason, the power supply for communications equipment must be independent of the mains power supply so that it continues working if the mains power fails.

The most common form of communication between the surface and the tunnelling face is either by radio or a tannoy system.

Lone working should **not** be allowed in tunnels because if you are taken ill or have an accident you may not be able to communicate.

It is critically important that you report any defects (such as damaged ventilation ducting) to a supervisor as soon as possible.

Safe access and egress

In tunnelling operations getting to and from a place of work safely, is as important as working safely whilst there.

Some things to consider are listed below.

☑ Fitting secure barriers of at least 1.2 m in height around every shaft, to prevent falls.

☑ Every working shaft must have a minimum of two escape methods or routes from each place where people are working.

☑ A tally system must be in place to control entry and exit to any tunnel under construction.

☑ The **maximum** distances between safe refuges in a tunnel are, 50 m on straight sections and 25 m on curved sections.

☑ Man-riding cages must not be overloaded. A label or notice will state the maximum number of people that can be carried.

☑ Safety nets and/or sliding doors must be fitted to man-riding cages/hoists/baskets to prevent anyone falling out or leaning out whilst they are in motion.

☑ Vertical ladders in tunnel shafts must have a landing (resting place) every 6 m.

☒ For maintenance purposes, water must not be allowed to accumulate above rail level in a tunnel.

F
23

Emergency actions

In effect tunnels are confined spaces requiring, in most cases, that a self-rescue set is made available to each worker. Where one is provided, you should be aware of the following.

☑ It must be immediately available at all times.

☑ The duration of the air supply will be significantly reduced if you exert yourself whilst wearing it (such as when running).

☑ At best the air supply will only last for 20 minutes.

In an emergency the rescue services will use the tally board to find out who is underground. A tally system counts people in and people out.

If there is an emergency or fire, if possible raise the alarm, and if safe to do so leave the tunnel.

If the ventilation system failure alarm activates you should immediately evacuate the workplace.

Fire and hot works

An underground fire can have devastating consequences. The close control of fire risks (such as those listed below) is therefore essential.

☑ Fire checks must be maintained for at least 60 minutes after any hot works have ceased.

☒ Smoking, or even the carrying of smoking materials, is not permitted underground.

☒ Smoking or other naked flames are not permitted within **10 m** of battery charging areas because of the flammable gas produced by lead-acid batteries when they are charging.

☒ Hot works are not permitted within **10 m** of any diesel fuelling point or lead-acid battery charging area.

Electrical safety

Emergency lighting must be installed in tunnels and must come on if the main lighting fails. The maximum distance between emergency lighting units is **50 m**.

For personal safety, apart from battery-operated tools, all powered hand tools must operate from a 110 volt supply.

Industrial electrical plugs and sockets are colour coded to show what voltage they are carrying.

Yellow	110 volt.
Blue	230 volt.
Red	400 volt.

F
23

Atmosphere

In tunnelling a safe, breathable atmosphere cannot be guaranteed unless suitable control measures are taken.

Using the right equipment is essential to avoid creating hazardous atmospheres.

☑ Only use intrinsically safe (spark proof) electrical and other equipment to limit the risk of ignition of any potentially explosive or flammable atmosphere that may form.

☑ All diesel or electrically powered plant must be fitted with a **fixed** fire extinguishing system.

☒ **Not** using petrol-powered internal combustion engines. This will reduce the potential for a flammable atmosphere to form, and limit the potential for an increase in carbon monoxide.

Maintaining a satisfactory level of oxygen in the air is essential. Normally, there is 21% oxygen in the air we breathe. Oxygen deficiency, which causes breathlessness, occurs if the level falls below 19%.

There are potential dangers from other gases that may be found underground.

☑ Exposure to **hydrogen sulphide** can kill through respiratory paralysis. It smells like rotten eggs and so its presence should be immediately obvious. Hydrogen sulphide effectively paralyses the nerves in the nose, leading people to believe that if they can no longer smell the gas and that it has disappeared when it has not.

☑ Naturally occurring **methane** is highly flammable, and can combine with the oxygen in the air, to form an explosive mixture.

☑ Exposure to **carbon monoxide** prevents the intake of oxygen into the body.

☑ **Nitrogen oxide**, which is produced by diesel-powered equipment, can cause breathing problems.

 The use of a calibrated multi-gas monitor is a reliable way of detecting the presence of methane and carbon monoxide.

Forced ventilation is one way of limiting the potential build up of hazardous gases underground. The failure of ventilation equipment must be indicated by an audible and visual alarm and should trigger an immediate and managed evacuation of the workplace.

Health risks

Tunnelling work will sometimes involve working in a compressed air environment. Decompression illness, often shortened to DCI, is a potential health risk.

Concrete and cement batching plants must be equipped with an eyewash station to provide quick treatment to anyone who has concrete splashed onto their face.

The following health risks are associated with sprayed concrete linings.

☑ Cement burns.

☑ Hand-arm vibration syndrome.

☑ Inhalation of dust.

The following are some of the hazards and risks associated with hand-mining.

☑ Hand-arm vibration syndrome.

☑ Noise.

☑ Inhalation of dust.

☑ Roof falls, falling mined and other materials.

Hand-arm vibration syndrome (HAVS) is caused by a combination of the level of vibration and the duration and frequency of the exposure time. The effects of HAVS, which includes damage to the nerves and blood vessels in the hand, cannot be cured.

Equipment and moving plant

The movement or operation of plant in close proximity to where people are working will create a potentially dangerous situation unless a safe separation is maintained. Working in the confines of a tunnel can make this difficult to achieve. Below are some examples of good practice.

☑ Crush zones caused by moving plant will be indicated by:
  – flashing warning lights
  – signs or barriers.

☑ All conveyors must be fitted with:
  – an audible alarm to indicate that it is about to start
  – an emergency stop system (pull cord or button).

☑ Inclined conveyors must be fitted with an anti roll-back device to prevent the belt running backwards if power is lost.

☑ Ensuring that segment erectors have a fail-safe device to stop the operation if the equipment experiences one of the following problems.
  – Suffers any malfunction.
  – Develops a leak.
  – Suffers a power supply failure.

☑ Fitting audible and/or visible alarms to rams and erectors of tunnel boring machines or hydraulic jacking rams in pipe-jacking shafts/pits, to warn when they are moving.

☑ An additional control point is the most effective way of overcoming the restricted vision of tunnel boring machine (TBM) operators during the building process.

☑ Always using a hop up or refuge in a tunnel when vehicles are passing.

☑ Always go immediately to a hop up or refuge if a locomotive or other vehicle is approaching.

☑ The lights fitted to locomotives must be:
  – visible at a minimum distance of **60 m**
  – white (if fitted) to the front of the locomotive
  – red (if fitted) to the rear of the locomotive.

A student learning how to drive a tunnelling locomotive

F
23

☑ Secondary couplings must be fitted to un-braked rolling stock to reduce the risk of it running away.

☑ In an emergency a locomotive must be able to stop with a distance not exceeding **60 m**.

☑ Ideally, the movement of locomotives when entering the back of a TBM will be controlled by:
  – traffic lights
  – closed circuit television (CCTV) in the cab.

☑ The traffic light system used to control plant movement underground is as follows.
  – **Red** – stop.
  – **Amber** – out bye.
  – **Green** – in bye.

Pipework, services and hoses under pressure

All services running through the tunnel should be safely positioned to avoid them being damaged. The use of pressure systems is potentially hazardous unless safe work practices (such as those listed below) are adopted.

☑ Isolating or releasing stored energy before disconnecting or uncoupling tunnel services.

☑ Include isolation arrangements in the safe system of work for maintenance work on grouting or slurry lines, especially if removing guards.

☑ The fitting of anti-whip devices across flexible hose connections to prevent the ends flying about if they become disconnected under pressure.

☑ Being aware that pumped grouting and sprayed concrete operations can result in the following.
  – Injury resulting from burst hoses.
  – Injury resulting from blowout at the injection point.
  – Hearing damage and loss through exposure to excessive noise levels.

☑ Immediately releasing the pressure if a grouting or sprayed concrete hose becomes blocked.

☑ Cleaning grouting pipelines after use to prevent blockages and bursting when they are used again.

☑ Replacing hoses that show signs of swelling, which suggests they are damaged.

☑ Being aware that hoses, which are of a similar size but with different markings, are **not** interchangeable. Although hoses may appear similar, they may have one of the following attributes.
  – Have different operating capacities.
  – Be for different uses.
  – Be of different physical sizes.

F
23

24
Plumbing (JIB)

What your site and employer should do for you

1. Ensure that a competent person supervises the work.
2. Inform you of the significant hazards identified in the risk assessment.
3. Provide you with a method of working that is safe and without risks to your health.
4. The safe way of working will be in a method statement which will be explained to you.
5. Provide you with adequate instruction and training.
6. At no time place you in danger.

What you should do for your site and employer

1. Follow the agreed safe system of work.
2. Keep to any permit systems which are in operation.
3. Not take risks with your own or anyone else's health or safety.
4. Report any aspect of your work which you feel is unsafe.

F
24

Introduction

Plumbing and gas-related work is highly specialised and potentially dangerous. All such work must be properly planned, only carried out by trained and competent contractors and be adequately supervised as necessary.

No-one should attempt to work on any fuel gas pipework or equipment unless they are a Gas Safe registered engineer.

 Poorly thought out or executed gas-related work activities can kill.

Safe methods of working

Safe working must include attention to the following.

☑ Looking after equipment and hand tools to ensure they are safe to use, including carrying out simple repairs (such as replacing a split file handle) where this is practical.

☑ Being aware that cutting large diameter pipes will leave extremely sharp edges.

☑ Leaving all places of work in a safe condition if they have to be left unoccupied, particularly if working on fuel gas systems in domestic premises where the occupier will not be risk-aware.

☑ Making sure there is safe access to any place of work and that the workplace itself is safe to occupy (for example using a ladder or stepladder if accessing the loft space of a domestic premises and making sure that there is safe access over the joists).

☑ Carrying out the transportation of people, equipment and materials in a safe and responsible manner, examples are listed below.

   – Only carrying people in the back of a van if it is fitted with factory-fitted seats and seat belts.

   – Carrying long lengths of tubing in a suitable pipe-rack attached to the roof of a van.

   – Always wearing a seat belt, when one is provided, if operating construction plant.

☑ If the sides of an excavation are not supported and show signs of collapse, it must not be entered by any person.

 Readers of this chapter should also refer to the 'Common elements' section of Chapter F25 Heating, ventilation, air conditioning and refrigeration (HVACR).

F
24

For further guidance refer to:

Joint Industry Board PMES England & Wales
Lovell House, Sandpiper Court
Phoenix Business Park
Eaton Socon
St Neots
Cambridge
PE19 8EP

Tel: 01480 476925

www.jib-pmes-org

F
24

25

Heating, ventilation, air conditioning and refrigeration (HVACR)

What your site and employer should do for you

1. Make sure that a competent person will supervise the work.

2. Tell you about the significant hazards identified in the risk assessment.

3. Provide you with a method of working that is safe and without risks to your health.

4. Explain the safe way of working to you in a method statement.

5. Provide you with adequate instruction, training and supervision.

6. At no time expect you to work unsafely or work in a place of danger.

What you should do for your site and employer

1. Follow the agreed safe system of work.

2. Comply with any permit systems that are in operation.

3. Not take risks with your own or anyone else's health or safety.

4. Report any aspect of your work which you feel is unsafe.

Introduction

Common heating, ventilation, air conditioning and refrigeration (HVACR) elements below should be read by people from the following trades.

- ☑ Domestic heating and plumbing services (HAPS).
- ☑ Pipefitting and welding (industrial and commercial) (PFW).
- ☑ Ductwork (DUCT).
- ☑ Refrigeration and air conditioning (RAAC).
- ☑ Services and facilities maintenance (SAF).

You should also read the section later in the chapter that refers to your particular trade.

Common HVACR elements

Competency

Competency is essential if work is to be carried out in a way which is safe and, so far as is reasonably practicable, free of risks to health and safety. Competency can be defined as a combination of training, knowledge, attitude, experience and skills.

Competency is a 'two-way street'.

- ☑ No-one should ask any other person to carry out a job unless they know that the other person is competent, adequately resourced and able to carry it out in a way that is safe and without risks to health.
- ☑ No person should accept any job unless they know that they are competent and have the resources to carry it out in a way that is safe and without risks to health.

Examples of good practice are listed below.

- ☑ All work must be properly planned in advance, with the risks assessed and eliminated or controlled.
- ☑ Only Gas Safe registered engineers are authorised to work on fuel gas pipework or components.
- ☑ Dangerous fuel or other gas fittings that could cause a death or major injury must be reported to the Health and Safety Executive.
- ☑ The pressure testing of pipework and vessels must only be carried out by someone who is trained, competent and authorised.
- ☑ All power tools must be used in a safe and responsible way.
- ☑ Only people who are trained, competent and authorised and work for an F-gas registered company are allowed to install, service or maintain systems that contain or are designed to contain refrigerant gases.
- ☑ Anyone who is concerned over their own or anyone else's health or safety must report it to someone in authority on the site.

F
25

Hot work

Hot work presents the obvious risk of fire. Many serious fires have occurred because the risks were not properly managed. All hot works must be planned for and managed correctly. One way of managing the risk of fire resulting from hot works is the implementation and policing of a hot-works permit system. Anyone planning to carry out hot works that involve the use of a blow torch or hot air gun should make sure of the following.

☑ Seek authority and agreement from site management.

☑ Obtain approval from your supervisor or site manager.

☑ Make sure that an extinguisher of the correct type is available in the immediate area.

☑ Remove lagging from pipework for at least 1 m either side of where work will be carried out on lagged pipes.

☑ Use a mat of a non-combustible material when a blowtorch is used near to any combustible materials (such as timber).

☑ Stop any work involving the use of a blowtorch at least one hour before leaving the job and inspect the area before leaving.

☑ When the task is complete, report to site management.

☑ Notify your supervisor or site manager when the hot works are completed.

Anyone planning hot works must implement a hot-work permit scheme and make sure it is followed.

Checking, installing, testing and commissioning installations

☑ Plant and equipment must be installed, tested and commissioned in such a way that it is safe to use.

☑ It is essential that the unauthorised use of plant and equipment is prevented, if necessary by the locking off of switches and valves, until such time as it has been fully commissioned.

Confined spaces and risers

Confined space working is recognised as being particularly hazardous.

☑ No-one should enter a confined space unless:
  – a risk assessment has been carried out
  – a method statement has been prepared
  – if required by the site or the employing organisation rules and procedures, a permit to work has been issued.

☑ Other ways of doing the job must always be investigated before entry is made.

☑ The use of hazardous substances, which can be breathed in, must be closely controlled in confined spaces.

Danger
Confined space

No unauthorised entry

Permit to work must be obtained

F
25

☑ Carrying out confined space working in an unsafe way has been the cause of many deaths, many by people who were trying to perform rescues for which they were not trained or equipped.

☑ If a naturally occurring toxic or flammable gas, such as hydrogen sulphide (H2S) or methane (CH4) is detected, the space must be evacuated immediately.

☑ Potential failure of the lighting in a confined space must be controlled by issuing workers with intrinsically safe torches, as a minimum.

☑ If oxyacetylene equipment is used in a confined space, the two main safety considerations are the following.

– Unburnt oxygen causing an oxygen enriched atmosphere.

– A flammable gas leak.

It must be understood that simply providing forced ventilation may not create or provide respirable (safe to breathe) air.

Electrical safety

Electricity can kill. It cannot be detected by any of the senses except touch. Working close to or near exposed live electrical circuits can result in a fatal shock. Here are some examples of good practice in electrical safety.

☑ Defective electrical equipment, including hand tools, must be taken out of service immediately and a procedure put in place to make sure they cannot be used.

☑ Extension leads must be run out in a safe way so that they do not overheat and are not a tripping hazard. If possible run them above head height or along the join of the walls and the floor.

☑ Electrical distribution circuits must only be installed by competent and authorised electrical contractors.

☑ If the supply system does not meet your needs, tell someone and then stop work until an authorised supply has been installed.

☑ All portable (230 volt) and 110 volt equipment must be periodically tested for electrical safety PAT (portable appliance test), commonly known as 'PAT testing'.

☑ Battery-powered tools do not need testing although mains-powered battery chargers do.

☑ Temporary continuity bonding must be installed before breaking into metal pipework to provide a continuous earth for the installation throughout the duration of the work.

☑ Ideally, only battery-powered hand tools should be used to carry out work outside in wet weather.

☑ Testing for hidden cables within the structure of a wall should be carried out, using a cable tracer, before disturbing the fabric of the wall.

F
25

Heating, ventilation, air conditioning and refrigeration (HVACR)

☑ Carry out the following before working on electrically powered equipment.
  – Make sure the equipment is switched off.
  – Isolate the supply at the main board.
  – Lock out and tag the circuit at the main supply board.
  – Prove the circuit dead with a GS38 proving unit and test instrument.

☑ If work has to be carried out on electrical equipment and the main isolator does not have a lock out device, the person(s) doing the job should carry out the following.
  – Identify if the circuit to be worked on is fed from a single or multiple supply.
  – Using appropriate methods isolate the circuit from all sources of supply.
  – Secure the means of isolation.
  – Display clear warning signs at the isolators that the equipment is being worked on and must not be energised.

☑ If working on or near to live exposed conductors, a safe system of work (including a permit to work) should be in place in accordance with the requirements of the Electricity at Work regulations.

☑ The use of 110 volt power tools is preferred on site because they are safer; transformers are used to reduce the 230 volt supply to 110 volts.

☑ Electrical power cables are often colour coded – 110 volt (yellow), 230 volt (blue) and 400 volt (red).

☑ When assembling a mobile access tower, overhead electrical cables must be treated as live until it is confirmed that they are dead.

☑ No-one, other than competent persons engaged on authorised work must work on or near to exposed electrical conductors unless they are confirmed to be dead. Damaged cables must be isolated and replaced.

☑ The padlock to an electrical lock-out guard can be fitted by anyone working on the equipment. However, only competent and authorised persons should work on electrical distribution systems.

☑ If the mains isolator for a piece of equipment is found switched off upon arrival on site, work must **not** start until the person in control of the premises has been consulted and the item is proven to be disconnected from all electrical supplies. Secured disconnection (isolation) should be achieved.

☑ Adequate task lighting must be provided, where there is not enough natural light to allow any job to be carried out safely.

Emergency situations

You may find that you are first on the scene following an accident to another worker, and it is important that you know what to do. Carry out the following if you find anyone who is injured.

☑ Make sure that you are not in any danger.

☑ Stay with the victim, keep them still and send someone else to find a first aider.

It is important that everyone on site knows what to do in an emergency situation. A serious emergency may result in the evacuation of the whole site.

☑ If a natural gas leak in an enclosed area is reported, the area should be ventilated and the gas emergency service should be contacted.

☑ The following steps must be taken if a refrigerant leak is reported in an enclosed area.
   – The area must be ventilated.
   – All naked flames must be extinguished.
   – It must be established whether or not it is safe to enter the area before anyone tries to do so.

Health risks

Health risks are often overlooked because the symptoms are not often immediately obvious. Examples of health risks that may have to be managed are listed below.

☑ Asbestos is likely to be found in any building built before the year 2000.

☑ Anyone who is likely to disturb asbestos should be trained, the training must be suitable for the work being undertaken and must be refreshed annually.

☑ Anyone who is likely to disturb the fabric of a building must be aware of the following.
   – Asbestos could be present.
   – Asbestos can be found in many places.
   – Asbestos containing materials (ACMs) and products include insulation boards around radiators, gaskets and seals in joints, and rope seals in a boiler.
   – If the presence of asbestos is suspected, work must stop immediately and the situation must be reported to a supervisor or manager.
   Note: the asbestos register must be consulted before the work starts.

☑ Anyone suffering from headache or sickness whilst using a solvent-based product (such as an adhesive) should be taken into fresh air. They will also need first-aid treatment, and the incident should be reported.

☑ Discarded items of drug-using equipment (for example hypodermic needles) must be safely removed by wearing gloves and using grips if practical. The supervisor or manager must be told and the incident should be reported internally.

☑ Manual handling must be carried out in a way that avoids injury.
   – Generally assessing the task as a whole before trying to lift items.
   – Operatives telling their supervisor and asking for help if required to move any load that they know is too heavy for them to move without help.
   – Using a suitable manual handling aid, (such as a trolley) if needed, to move loads, particularly over long distances.

☑ Repeatedly bending copper tube over the knees using an internal spring could result in long-term damage to the knees.

☑ Noise assessments must be carried out by a competent person to assess if there is a danger of noise-induced hearing loss.

F
25

Heating, ventilation, air conditioning and refrigeration (HVACR)

☑ When carrying out solvent welding on plastic ductwork it is essential that the area remains well ventilated and that the appropriate respiratory protective equipment (RPE) is worn.

☑ You can avoid risks to health from working with lead by carrying out the following.
  - Not smoking whilst bossing or otherwise handling it.
  - Preventing it from getting into the bloodstream by washing your hands after handling it.

☑ The potentially fatal risk from legionella can be controlled by being aware of the following.
  - The ideal temperature range for the bacteria to breed is between 20°C and 45°C.
  - Breeding grounds for legionella include slow-moving or stationary water supplies (such as infrequently used shower heads or 'dead legs') that are within the above temperature range.
  - The bacteria is spread to humans through breathing in water droplets in the form of fine mists and sprays.
  - Suitable respiratory protective equipment (RPE) with a protection factor of 40 must be worn when breaking into the system if exposure to sprays or mists cannot be prevented.
  - If a case of legionella is suspected, the Health and Safety Executive must be informed immediately.

LPG and other gases

LPG is a flammable and explosive gas that is often found on construction sites. Like many other compressed gases it is dangerous if not handled and stored properly. Some safety precautions are listed below.

☑ LPG cylinders that supply site cabins must be kept outside of the cabin.

☑ LPG and acetylene cylinders must be stored in the open air to prevent the build-up of leaking gas.

☑ If LPG cylinders are transported and/or stored overnight in a van, there must be a low-level drainage route to the outside to protect against the accumulation of leaking LPG.

LPG store

☑ Where LPG cylinders are being transported in a van they must be carried in a purpose-built container inside the vehicle and have an LPG sign on the outside of the vehicle.

☑ Anyone who has to transport more than 5 kg of LPG in a covered van must be trained and competent in the hazards relating to the gases.

☑ It is important to know the difference between equipment that is used on propane and butane because propane equipment works on a higher pressure.

☑ LPG is heavier than air and leaking gas will collect at the lowest point it can reach (such as basements, drains or gulleys).

☑ Except for cylinders designed for use on gas-powered forklift trucks, store all LPG cylinders in an upright position to prevent the liquid gas being drawn from the cylinder creating a hazardous situation.

F
25

- ☑ If a leak is suspected in any part of an LPG system efforts to trace it must only be made using a proper leak detection fluid.
- ☑ Oxygen cylinders must be handled with great care due to the high pressure to which they are filled.
- ☑ Ensure the following when using oxy-acetylene equipment.
  - The cylinders must be secured in an upright position.
  - The cylinders, hoses and flashback arrestors must be in good condition.
  - The area must be well ventilated and clear of any obstructions.
  - The cylinders must be stored separate from other gas cylinders in a special compound.
  - It should not be used for jointing copper tube using capillary soldered fittings.
  - It should not be used for fitting capillary soldered fittings to copper tubing.
- ☑ Acetylene cylinders must also be stored away from other flammable and combustion supporting gases, outside in a special storage compound.
- ☑ It is important to be able to identify the content of gas cylinders by their colour. For this reason they are colour coded.
  - Propane cylinders are red or orange.
  - Butane cylinders are blue.
  - Acetylene cylinders are maroon.
- ☑ Where welding is being carried out, screens must be provided to protect others from welding flash.

Lifting operations

Lifting operations have been the cause of many accidents because they were not properly planned, carried out or defective equipment was used. Everyone involved in lifting operations must be aware of the following.

- ☑ The sequence of operations in any lifting activity must be laid out in advance in a method statement (called a lift plan).
- ☑ The safe working load (SWL) of any piece of lifting equipment or accessory must never be exceeded.
- ☑ Every piece of lifting equipment and each lifting accessory must be marked with its SWL.
- ☑ If any item of lifting equipment is found to be defective the equipment must not be used, the item should be placed in quarantine and the problem reported to a supervisor or manager.
- ☑ All lifting equipment must be stable and secure when being used.
- ☑ Items that are lifted into a place where they will be installed must not be released from the lifting equipment until securely fixed in place.

F
25

All lifting equipment must be thoroughly examined periodically by a competent person.

Lifting accessories (such as chains, strops and lifting eyes) and lifting equipment used to lift or lower people must be thoroughly examined every six months. All other lifting equipment must be thoroughly examined every 12 months.

Personal protective equipment

Wearing the correct personal protective equipment (PPE) can prevent exposure to harmful substances. The wrong type of PPE is unlikely to provide protection from a specified hazard. PPE should always be considered as a last resort (for example, when a risk remains that cannot be controlled by other means higher up the hierarchy of preventative and protective measures). Wear the following types of PPE in the situations described.

☑ The correct type of impact resistant eye protection when drilling, cutting or grinding any material that could produce flying debris.

☑ Thermally protective gloves to avoid direct skin contact with pipe-freezing equipment. Always read the control of substances hazardous to health (COSHH) assessment for the product.

☑ A safety helmet, protective footwear, hearing protection, suitable respiratory protective equipment (RPE) and eye protection when using a hammer drill.

☑ Ear defenders if working in a noisy environment or doing any job in which high levels of noise are produced.

☑ Suitable eye protection if carrying out oxy-acetylene welding.

☑ Safety gloves, suitable RPE, and eye protection if having to handle fibreglass roof insulation.

☑ RPE when using hazardous substances that can be breathed in. Do not start work if this hasn't been provided.

☑ Cut-resistant gloves when handling anything with sharp edges.

Personal protective equipment should only be considered as a last resort.

Half face mask

Safety gloves

Safe methods of work

The importance of adopting safe methods of work, derived from a risk assessment and given in a method statement or similar document cannot be overstated. Some examples are shown below.

☑ The correct hand tools must be used for any job (such as using a hammer and bolster chisel for taking up floorboards).

☑ The transportation of tools and materials must be carried out in a safe and responsible way, examples are below.

  – Carrying long lengths of tubing in a pipe-rack attached to the roof of a van.

  – Fixing a ladder to the roof rack of a van using proper ladder-clamps.

☑ The exhaust fumes from vehicle exhausts are toxic; if internal combustion engine-driven plant has to be run inside a building, the exhaust fumes must be extracted to a position outside the building.

☑ Prevent contact with moving parts of machinery or rotating materials by enclosing them with guards or barriers.

☑ Be aware of sharp edges when cutting through sheet material or pipes.

☑ Keep unauthorised people out of the area when pressure testing pipework or vessels.

☑ Prevent the entanglement of clothing when using any rotating machine.

☑ A permit to work system should be introduced for all high risk work activities.

☑ Before starting work on any piece of equipment it is essential that the operation and maintenance manual for the equipment is consulted.

☑ To prevent unauthorised access to plant and switchgear rooms the doors must always be kept locked and only competent and authorised persons should be able to access them.

☑ Where possible lone working should be avoided. A lone worker must register their presence with their site management or site representative before starting work and a system of periodically checking on the lone worker must be in place.

☑ Spilled liquids, for example oils and greases can create a slip trip hazard. Refuelling and decanting should be carried out in an approved place using nozzles, funnels and on a spill mat if possible. If a spill does occur tell your supervisor and keep people out of the area until it is cleaned up.

Do not carry out tasks in an improvised way. Only ever use the correct tool for the job.

Working at height

Examples of good practice for safe working at height are listed below.

☑ A risk assessment must have been carried out.

☑ If a ladder is used it should be secured to the structure against which it is resting to prevent it from slipping.

F
25

☑ When using a stepladder the restraining mechanism must be fully extended.

☑ Stepladders must only be used in the following situations.

- If a risk assessment shows they are suitable for the job.
- They are in good condition.
- For light, short-term work (lasting no more than a few minutes) that does not involve stretching or reaching.
- Where the work does not involve twisting the torso if you cannot face the work, and work from a stepladder is the wrong platform.

Proprietary access system with ladder access, working platform, guard-rails and hoist

☑ When a mobile access tower is used, only one working platform should be occupied at any one time.

☑ When deciding the maximum height to which a mobile access tower may be built the manufacturer's instructions must be referred to.

☑ The hatch of a mobile access tower working platform must be closed immediately after gaining access to the platform.

☑ Before moving a mobile access tower, all people, tools and equipment must be removed from the working platform.

☑ The users of mobile access towers must be aware of the proximity of overhead live electric cables before erecting the tower.

☑ Edge protection must be fitted to working platforms to prevent the fall of a person or object.

☑ A stable working platform (such as a mobile access tower) should be used for jobs where there is a good floor surface and 'heavier' type work is to be carried out at height.

☑ Ladders used on site must be labelled 'Class 1' (industrial). 'Class 2' or 'BS EN 131' (light trade) or 'Class 3' (domestic use only) must not be used.

☑ Wooden ladders that have been painted must not be used because the paint can hide defects.

☑ All shafts, pits, service ducts, large floor voids and so on, must be fitted with double guard-rails and toe-boards or a secure cover if someone could fall into them.

☑ If working at height to dismantle lengths of soil pipe, it can be safely carried out by working in pairs and breaking the length at the collar to remove complete sections.

☑ Flue liners must be installed in a safe way by working in pairs at roof level and using a safe method of access (such as a chimney scaffold).

☑ Objects must not be thrown or dropped from height and must be prevented from falling.

☑ As far as practical, using a ladder to access ceiling voids or soffits containing a large number of services should be restricted. Other means of access may be needed.

☒ Never use utility service pipes or cables as a make-shift working platform or a means of access.

F
25

Domestic heating and plumbing services (HAPS)

Installing or maintaining heating and plumbing services can present the risk of injury or ill health. Some examples of good practice are listed below.

- ☑ Temporary continuity bonding should be carried out before removing and replacing sections of metallic pipework to provide a continuous earth for the installation.
- ☑ When welding is being carried out, a screen should be provided to protect others from welding flash.
- ☑ The most likely risk of injury when cutting a pipe is because the edge of the cut pipe becomes sharp to touch.
- ☑ When transporting long lengths of pipe by van use a pipe rack fixed to the roof of the van. Ladder clamps should be used to secure a ladder or stepladders to the roof rack of a van.
- ☑ When taking up a length of floorboard to install pipework you should use a hammer and bolster (and not a hammer with a chisel or screwdriver).

> **If a job involves work below a ground-level suspended timber floor, you should first check or ask if the work could be performed from outside it, rather than entering a potentially confined space with restricted working room.**

Pipefitting and welding (industrial and commercial) (PFW)

Pipefitting and welding can present the risk of injury or ill health to you and others. Some examples of good practice are listed below.

- ☑ When using a pipe threading machine a safety barrier should be erected around the whole length of the pipe and you should make sure that your clothing cannot get caught on rotating parts of the machine. In accordance with the requirements of the Provision and Use of Work Equipment Regulations (PUWER) all dangerous parts of machines shall, so far as is reasonably practicable, be fenced/guarded.
- ☑ When a new piece of plant has been installed but has not been commissioned, it should be left with all valves and switches locked off.
- ☑ Before using oxyacetylene equipment it is essential to check the following.
  - The cylinders, hoses and flashback arresters are in good condition.
  - The area is well ventilated and clear of any obstructions.
- ☑ Acetylene cylinders (maroon in colour) should be stored outside in a special storage compound when not in use.
- ☑ When using oxyacetylene brazing equipment, the cylinders should be stood upright and secured, preferably on a purpose made trolley.
- ☑ When using pipe-freezing equipment to isolate the damaged section of pipe, you should read the COSHH assessment and wear appropriate PPE and RPE.

Only those involved in carrying out the pressure testing of pipework or vessels should be present.

F
25

Ductwork (DUCT)

Installing or maintaining ductwork can present the risk of injury or ill health. Some examples of good practice are listed below.

☑ Before painting the external surface of any ductwork, you should read the COSHH assessment for the paint.

☑ Fume extraction must be provided when welding or carrying out other hot work on galvanised ductwork.

☑ Before using a solvent based adhesive on ductwork you must:
  – read the (manufacturer's) safety data sheet and the Control of Substances Hazardous to Health (COSHH) assessment
  – establish a safe working area
  – comply with the COSHH assessment (for example, the creation of confined spaces conditions, ventilation, PPE, smoking, and sources of ignition).

☑ If, before fitting, a defect is noticed in any component of a system that is being installed, the item must not be fitted and you must tell your supervisor or manager.

☑ Before using a cleaning agent or biocide on a ductwork system:
  – read the (manufacturer's) safety data sheet and the Control of Substances Hazardous to Health (COSHH) Assessment.
  – consult with the building occupier and establish a safe working area and conditions, safe for yourself and for others
  – produce a method statement for the work in compliance with the COSHH assessment (for example, the creation of confined spaces conditions, ventilation, PPE, smoking and sources of ignition).

☑ Before cleaning a system in an industrial laboratory or other premises where harmful particulates might be encountered:
  – the system must be inspected
  – samples must be collected from the system
  – a job-specific risk assessment and method statement must be prepared.

☑ If it is necessary for a person to enter ductwork, two items that must be considered are the:
  – dangers of working in confined spaces
  – strength of the ductwork and its supports.

☑ Before working on a kitchen extraction system, the nature of the cooking deposits in the system should be established.

☑ Aluminium ductwork that has been pre-insulated with fibreglass must only be cut using tin snips, with the person doing the cutting wearing suitable PPE and RPE.

☑ When jointing plastic-coated metal ductwork, welding presents far greater health risks than, for example, riveting, taping or using nuts and bolts.

 If dismantling extract ductwork, it is essential to find out what it may be contaminated with before starting work.

Refrigeration and air conditioning (RAAC)

Refrigerants and other gases

Most gases have the potential to cause harm because they are explosive, stored at high pressure, are at low temperatures or are harmful to the environment. Examples of good practice and the unsafe properties of gases are shown below.

☑ When not is use, refrigerant cylinders must be stored in a special, locked storage compound in the open air.

☑ Refrigerant gases are heavier than air and if released into an enclosed space will sink to the lowest place they can seep into.

☑ If transported in a van, cylinders of refrigerant gases must be carried in a purpose-built container inside the vehicle.

☑ When handling refrigerant gases, eye protection, overalls, thermal resistant gloves and safety boots must be worn.

☑ Flashback arrestors must be fitted between pipes and gauges of oxy-propane brazing equipment.

☑ Ensure you check the following when pressure testing using nitrogen.
   - The gauges can take the necessary pressure.
   - The nitrogen cylinder is secured in an upright position.

☒ Oxygen must never be used for pressure testing because it could react with the oil in the compressor causing an explosion possibly resulting in serious injury or death.

Safe methods of work

☑ When a refrigerant leak has been reported in a closed area, it must be established that it is safe to enter before anyone tries to do so.

☑ Before entering a cold-room it must be established that the exit door is fitted with an internal handle.

Services and facilities maintenance (SAF)

Checking, installing, testing and commissioning installations

Where new plant or equipment is being installed it must be done in a way that avoids injury to the people doing the job or anyone else. This must include ensuring that the plant or equipment cannot be operated in an unauthorised way or by unauthorised persons before it has been commissioned and handed over.

☑ The health and safety file for any building, where one has been compiled, is a possible useful source of information on the safe way of maintaining the systems within it.

☑ The temperature of the hot water at the tap furthest from the boiler should be at least 50°C within one minute of starting to run it.

F
25

☑ The maximum temperature of a cold water supply must be 20°C within two minutes of starting to run it.

☑ Where there is a cooling tower on site, it must be registered with the Local Authority and have a formal log book that is kept up to date.

☑ On cooling tower systems the water must be chemically treated.

☑ Make sure the following is carried out when replacing the filters in an air-conditioning system.

 – A job-specific risk assessment and method statement must be prepared and followed.

 – The person(s) doing the job must wear suitable overalls and a respirator.

☑ After a gas boiler has been serviced it must be checked for the following.

 – Flueing. 　　　　　　　　　　　– Gas rate.

 – Ventilation. 　　　　　　　　　– Safe functioning.

☑ Before adding an inhibitor to a heating system, the COSHH assessment for the product must be read and understood.

Pressure systems

The following are examples of designated pressure systems requiring a written scheme of examination and a safe systems of work under the pressure systems safety regulations 2000.

☑ Steam sterilising autoclave and associated pipework and protective devices.

☑ Steam boiler and associated pipework and protective devices.

☑ Gas-loaded hydraulic accumulator, if forming part of a pressure system.

☑ Portable hot water/steam-cleaning unit fitted with a pressure vessel.

☑ Vapour compression refrigeration system where the installed power exceeds 25 kW.

☑ Compressors and systems where the total volume of compressed gas in the system is in excess of 250 bar/ litres.

☑ Fixed LPG storage system supplying fuel for heating in a workplace.

F
25

Further information

Training record

Name of company _____

Name of employee _____

Name of supervisor _____

Instructions to supervisor

The employee and supervisor should sign each area of training listed below as it is completed. The manager responsible should endorse the record and ensure that a copy is retained on file.

	Date completed	Employee's signature	Supervisor's signature
1 General responsibilities			
2 Accident reporting and recording			
3 Health and welfare			
4 First aid and emergency procedures			
5 Personal protective equipment			
6 Asbestos			
7 Dust and fumes (Respiratory hazards)			
8 Noise and vibration			

	Date completed	Employee's signature	Supervisor's signature
9 Hazardous substances			
10 Manual handling			
11 Safety signs			
12 Fire prevention and control			
13 Electrical safety, tools and equipment			
14 Site transport safety			
15 Lifting operations and equipment			
16 Working at height			
17 Excavations and confined spaces			
18 Environmental awareness and waste control			
19 Demolition			
20 Highway works			
21 Specialist work at height			
22 Lifts and escalators			
23 Tunnelling			
24 Plumbing (JIB)			
25 Heating, ventilation, air conditioning and refrigeration (HVACR)			